THIS EARTH

A Second Volume of Essays
from an English Village

by

K. BRENDA MAGER

with illustrations by Colin Carr

This England Books
CHELTENHAM, GLOUCESTERSHIRE

First published in 1989
by This England Books,
73 Rodney Road Cheltenham Gloucestershire

Printed in Great Britain by
BPCC Wheatons Ltd, Exeter

ISBN 0 906324 11 4

CONTENTS

Foreword 4
'Old Billy Cloth-Cap' 6
Autumn Afternoon 10
The Park 14
The Holiday 16
The Meeting 22
Country Wedding 27
The Album 32
Summertime 37
Albert 40
'Miss' 45
Miss Myrtle and Miss Patience 49
From the Hilltop 53
The River 57
The Farm Sale 63
Morning 67
The Show 71
Easter Visit 76
Great-Grandma 80
The Family 84
Callers 89
The Tree House 94
Just Another Day 98
The Camp 104
Percy 110
Gifts 113
The Bone Setter 118
The Travelling Fair 123

FOREWORD

by Roy Faiers, Editor of This England

This is the second collection of essays from the
English countryside by K. Brenda Mager, a
farmer's wife who has been contributing a regular
"This Earth" column for *This England* magazine since its
inception in 1968. The first volume was printed in 1981
and proved to be an immediate success, the book being
quickly sold out as readers responded to the chance of
having Mrs. Mager's writings in more permanent form.
No reprint has been possible since then, but some of the
original essays have been used in educational textbooks
on the Continent as a means of bringing European lan-
guage students closer to the truth of English rural life.
Now comes this second volume, containing 27 different
essays, but all in the same vein, describing the characters
and local happenings which will be instantly recognisable
to all those who have experience of real village life in
England, as distinct from the contrived society generally
portrayed in travel brochures and television serials.

Readers who have lived in rural communities, far from
the sophisticated "urbanalities" of today, will readily call
to mind characters like Miss Myrtle and Miss Patience,
spinster sisters who keep the haberdashery shop. Miss
Myrtle, finicky with a duster and obsessed with invisible
dirt, was a "minx" in her young days . . . but her
cherished dreams of love died on the Somme. Then
there's "Old Billy Cloth-Cap", whose backwardness is
the butt of cruel taunts by village lads; and "Miss", the

aged schoolteacher who never threw off the armour of severity she clad herself with in order to control successive generations of country children.

In these gentle pages you can meet people from the past — everyday folk like Albert, Percy, household callers, farmers, travelling fair folk, and even the local bone-setter . . . all are here in a curious mixture which, despite the necessary cloak of anonymity, will remind you of true English country folk in all their splendid simplicity.

Regrettably, the pace of social change in the last fifty years has meant that they are now almost extinct. But they still live on in "this blessed plot, this earth, this realm" . . . and the pages of *This England*.

Colin Carr

'Old Billy Cloth-Cap'

T he cottage was dumpy; its thatched roof eye-
brow'd, the small windows that were deeply set
in ancient walls of mud and stud. Anyone care-
fully-footing the green-slimed path past the water-butt
might raise a steadying hand and touch bristled eaves —
eaves blackened and weathered by years. On past a mil-
dewed pink rose, and one came upon the open front
door, where a matful of sleeping cats absorbed the trap-
ped warmth.

Old Billy Cloth-Cap would be somewhere at work in
the summer-lush garden, his slight, bent figure almost
hidden by currant bushes and raspberry canes, easily
obscured by a rampant herbaceous border. Only the top
of his cap could sometimes be seen as he toiled with hoe

or rake or wheeled his capacious green barrow. It was a voluminous grey tweed cap, with segments converging under a button at the top. He wore it pulled well down to his ears in winter but now in summer it was mushroom-styled, shading his pudgy face. It was said that Mam had made the cap, also its companion (of like shape, but suitably black for funerals and Sundays). It was known, too, that he seldom removed the headgear, even when Mam scissored for him the grey straggles of hair that twice yearly encroached upon his collar. Village boys, idling in the lane beyond his garden, taunted him with another possible truth . . . "Old Billy Cloth-Cap! Wears it when he takes a nap!" they sang with lusty rudeness, ribald with the fortress of their youth and speed. The man shook his fist or sometimes threw lumps of soil harmlessly in their direction. The soil spattered into the hedge and his tormentors fled — their cruel laughter fading as they ran. Mercifully the mocking sound flitted as quickly from Billy's simple mind.

Once, in her buxom prime, she would have stormed outside and boxed their ears, but Mam now could no longer protect her Billy. In the restricted life, imprisoned by his handicap, he was, she realised, contented enough.

Billy, still her child, recognised no word and could not write. But he conspired with the earth, growing vegetables and fruit, as well as a splendour of flowers to feast their eyes. Birds came close to Billy as he worked — a blackbird watched from the cherry tree and one particular robin took crumbs from the work-scored hollow of his palm.

Soft hay, fragrant with meadow herbs, mounded the waggons. Then Billy led the horse between the cobs; the loader, aloft, braced himself against a supporting fork at the warning shout of "How'd ya!" as the brown mare was coaxed forward with scarcely a lurch.

Sparrow-hordes plundered the ripening corn in August, flying from hedges into the rustling wheat.

They picked grain from the ears, littering with husks the earth among the pimpernels. Billy's job was to walk the headlands, booted feet slipping and stumbling, and sweat beading his brow under the band of his cap. He shouted and sang, clapping two thin pieces of wood together as he walked. Sparrows, puzzled by the turnabout behaviour of their erstwhile friend, retreated until he passed; maybe they laughed, as did the teasing boys in the lane.

A stone bridge sturdily arched the gurgling brown river. There a gang of mallard plied for crust-pieces that Billy stored in his pocket. Their foolish, raucous quacking attracted a pirate flurry of marauding Muscovies from the farm. Billy guffawed. Duck-clamour and the man's braying overwhelmed the chuckle of the river. And no-one noticed the summer-sibilance of willow'd wind, as it came whispering from the water meadows.

Mam walked down the garden, a white basin in her hand. Billy, delighted, escorted her to the raspberry row. In the dairy, cool on the brick gantry, cream was yellow on the surface of milk in the earthenware pancheon. A toffee-gold Jersey cow, the provider, stood knee-deep in buttercups. Sooty lids, heavy-lashed, drooped over dark eyes and her tail constantly swished to sweep away biting flies. Soon Billy would fetch her up for evening milking — Mam would listen from the house and hear the gruff voice, droning from the shed. The cow, soothed by Billy's singing, stretched a rough tongue towards a corner of the washed-out raincoat that he always wore for milking; his cap was now worn back-to-front. Mam shook the cloth into place on the tea-table and took down cups from the dresser.

Billy was his own companion — with himself he was able happily to converse, never lonely in solitude. Sometimes he drove sheep or cattle along the lanes, over many dusty miles for a few pence — or merely for a slaking pint as reward. On the Common he allowed his charges peacefully to graze — with his back propped against the milestone. Billy sat and ate jam pasty from a brown paper bag. With humans, except for Mam, the man felt awkward — often they taunted and aggravated him to the point at which his temper spilled. Then gibberish burbled uncontrollably from his lips, clenched fists and windmill arms threatened that the limit had been reached. Fellow workers wandered prudently away, uncomprehending and afraid, leaving Billy alone at chaff-hole or muck-heap or to clear a blocked and stinking drain.

But with animals Billy was at ease and in command. Slobbering boar pig or red-eyed bull miraculously quietened at his approach; snarling mongrel-menace changed into tail-waving welcome, teeth-baring lips relaxed to a dog-smile at the sound of his voice.

On the pine dresser, Mam kept a pad of lined paper. Finding her flour supply dwindling in the bin, or counting only a few remaining blue bags of sugar, she licked her copying pencil to add items to her daily lengthening list. Haricot beans and sago, oatmeal for porridge, tape for new apron strings, winter mixtures and barley sugars for the sweet tin — when the page was filled, she and Billy walked the rutted lane to catch the 'bus on the turnpike road. When they returned, Billy was bowed by a burden of heavy bags, his chatter excited by the day's adventure.

Dusk crept kindly across the garden, where Old Billy Cloth-Cap sat on an apple-tree stump. Notes from a penny whistle shrilled into the moth-soft gloaming and, as though drawn by Pan pipes, two tabbies and a young black tom-cat ran purring to his side.

Autumn Afternoon

The almost-four-year old bent to push aside with with her hands the tangle of dying, jungled grass, thus making a path for small, wary feet in their ankle-strapped shoes. David, because he was two years bigger, stronger and braver (also two years less afraid of frogs) rushed ahead in bounding leaps, wellington'd legs kicking out sideways as he went. Helpfully he waved his arms and whooped and shouted, frightening for Judy the earwigs and the mice, and even the toad that had once betrayed itself at the last moment by a pulsation of its hideous, earth-hued form. Judy looked cautiously across the garden, lest a maned lion should be crouched, quivering, among tall golden ragworts and seeding heads of hemlock.

David reached the tree first, the favourite little tree that was only a year older than he was himself. Impatiently they had waited for sour green apples to be changed by sun and season to a blushing, polished red. Even Judy could touch the friendly branches and David showed her where blackbirds had pecked small cavities so scavenging wasps could follow into spoilt and fermenting fruit.

Mother followed the children, working the bramble

hedge that yielded juicy purple wealth to fill her enamel basin. This evening a bubbling brew of jam would add a few more jars to her larder shelf. Her hooked stick pulled and tugged at thorned and twining trails and Judy knew it would also chase away the tigers that might have lairs in the dense depths of the thicket.

A hazel bush, rough-leaved, held clusters of nuts; each nut was clothed with an elf-cap, fringed and green. Father, wearing his serious face, had this morning warned them to watch out for monkeys; though Judy looked and looked she saw only the wood-pigeon that exploded from the bush, scattering yellow leaves and shedding a small curling feather to rest, smoke-blue, on the brown cob of a dock plant. David expected monkeys no longer, for he learned Nature at school — and had seen Father wink at Mother when he spoke!

Soon Mother had filled her basin. She took the big old key from her apron pocket and opened the autumn-cob-webbed door. A fat spider sped across the grey wall and along the path — maybe it would return when they had gone, spin its repairs and lurk again in wait for blunder-ing, foolish victims.

The kitchen was dim and fusty-cold and Judy pressed closely against Mother. Even David spoke in a whisper, afraid that the house might hear him and take him pris-oner in its sad, strange silence. But Mother opened the parlour door and pushed wide the window. The sun smiled through and a peacock butterfly fluttered in with an inquisitive breeze. Rose-patterned curtains blew gaily and the matching cushions were plumped and tidy, just as Great-Great-Aunt would have liked to see them left.

It was David's turn to wind up the gramophone. From slots in the front of the wooden case came bouncy, squeaking music. Mother said it was an Irish Jig — it danced comfortingly through the house, waking it up and making it cheerful again, as it had been before Great-Great-Aunt had gone.

There was another record that the children liked, about a lion called Wallace and a boy who poked him in the ear with a stick — and, to David's delight, got eaten. Sometimes Mother took a new needle from a little tin: on the lid was a white smooth-haired terrier seated primly beside a wide-mouthed horn. Whenever the music slowed to a mournful dirge, David quickly turned the handle and the jig again merrily regained its momentum. The pile of dry sticks, gleaned from the garden, now crackled in the fireplace. Mother added some larger pieces and set the kettle to boil on the strengthening flames. Biscuits were kept in the round blue tin in the cupboard, but tomato sandwiches were wrapped, cool and damp, in a cloth parcel from home. There was sponge cake, too, and ripe bananas with speckled skins.

Reuben whistled loudly, tunelessly, into the house. The children ran to meet him, pulling him by both hands to join their feast. The gramophone was rewound and the old man swung Lucy to his hip; they whirled in mad, chuckling dance until, dizzy, they collapsed into a sheeted armchair. "Now, let's have a look at this window frame", he said, as soon as panting breath would allow and his mug was drained to the veriest dregs.

Taking a tape from the kangaroo-pocket of his hessian apron and a bit of pencil from behind his ear, he worked out some figures behind screwed-up eyes and then jotted them on a handy piece of grey card. To-morrow he would bring the necessary wood for the small repair. He admired, as he always did, the burr walnut table made generations ago, probably in a workshop scarcely different from his own. He showed the children how the lovely grain was wavy, blond, deep in the satiny wood.

The merest smear of her special home-made furniture polish, spread on the softest of cloths, had been sufficient to make a shine in which Great-Great-Aunt could proudly see the hazy reflection of her round, spectacled face. Reuben's work-hardened hands lingered reverently, lovingly, on the warm smooth surface. Then, visibly, he shook himself back to the September afternoon. "Now, lass, you wanted some help with the pears?"

The pear tree was ancient, obscuring the entire end of the house, thrusting above the gable and out beyond the sparrow'd eaves. The Williams hung in great greenish drops, just beginning to verge on gold. Reuben, up the ladder, twisted each fruit from the tree, then placed it tenderly in a basket.

There had always been bottled pears for Sunday tea at Great-Great-Aunt's, clove-fragrant and generously coated with cream that came thick and custard yellow from the brown stoneware jug. Reuben had gathered them each year and, as usual, he now descended the ladder although a few smaller fruits still dangled among the leaves. "The birds want a treat to help them into winter . . ." he told the children.

The sun was warm against the wall; Reuben sat on a wooden bench and took out his pipe and pouch. Mother came and draped a wet tea-towel over a currant bush to dry. The air was thick with sage-scent and the children laughed as they bit into fat-cheeked pears, bending over so that the juice ran onto the grass.

"Reuben", said Mother quietly, "I think she would be pleased to see us now". Contentedly she hung the basket over her arm. It would soon be time to walk home to make Father's tea, for the afternoon had happily slipped away.

The Park

The Park was bracken-brown. Slopes were loamy-dry, deep with pine needles; old sinewed oaks, that had gazed upon history's making, rustled paper leaves in October wind. A stream gurgled over its pebbled bed and bubbled along the shallows beneath shivering willows; long yellow leaves dropped lightly to the water and floated away like tiny narrow boats. Grey rocks jutted from wiry turf, sleeping where once they had erupted or perhaps been hurled by some dreadful volcanic upheaval.

A banshee wail, too hideous for such a splendid bird, echoed from the ruins where peafowl scratched and paraded, waiting for crumbs, raisins and admiration. Beyond were the ruins, red-bricked and sightless, comforted by seeding clumps of willow-herb and by ragwort brilliant still with many golden suns. Above, on the much-climbed hill, stood an arched tower around which the breeze from the forest swirled and blew.

Deer grazed, nervously watchful, spotted russet bodies blending with their surroundings. Larches, conceited in tufted beauty and wealthy with cones, clumped companionably in plantings; near a chained gate lingered the rank smell of fox, betraying a lair deeply secure behind old stone walls.

A little church watched over its graves, closely shading that of the child who had choked and died when he pushed a bead up his nose.

Thatched and latticed, whitewashed or tawny-bricked, cottages abutted the village street. Some faced the faraway town, others clustered near the rectory or stood privet-hedged round a bend. One was long and low, divided from the road by a strip of honey-brown pavement and a worn kerbstone. Many were at path-length, hiding behind clipped bushes and approached through a riot of dahlias and chrysanthemums; here there were joyously self-sown marigolds and banked nasturtiums, Red Admirals and hover-flies quivered and fed on Michaelmas Daisies and pink Sedum. Wasps buzzed drunkenly as they burrowed into fallen, rotting apples. Pears hung, fat and greenish-gold on wall-splayed trees. TEAS WITH HONEY, said the boards (or CREAM TEAS or HIGH TEAS) — Walnut Cottage had low ceilings and pot Geraniums — Lilac Cottage had a green gate and a gleaming brass doorknocker — Jasmine House was bigger and hid beehives behind the vegetable plot. Summer guests had sat in the parlour of Bluebell Farm and the children had crowded the windows to watch red-and-white cows lumbering into the yard for milking. The tables were set with pretty china and brown teapots, on cloths embroidered with hollyhocks and crinolined ladies.

Each tearoom had its speciality . . . wholemeal scones or cherry cake, or wild strawberry jam in cut-glass dishes. Mrs. Peberdy was famous for her gingerbread which was darkly sticky, and for her spectacles that were thicker than any that the children had ever seen. Miss Violet and Miss Mary had an Aberdeen terrier who must have spent most of the summer afternoons balanced on his square-clipped behind as he begged for biscuits.

At the end of the village was the Post Office and Shop, its summer trade expanded by the sale of glasses of home-made lemonade and of frozen-custard ice cream that was scooped into cornets or sandwiched, creamy-yellow, between wafers. Outside was a rack of glossy postcards with picturesque views of the village and the Park.

A 'bus groaned up the hill, its passengers looking into windows in which lights were already lit. A Barn Owl stood upright on a gate-post, eyes impassive in heart-shaped face . . . dead chestnut leaves fluttered in the gutter. Day grew tired and slumbered; the Park was left with its wildness and its ghosts . . .   □

The Holiday

Auntie Martha, her silk-bloused back to the engine, was knitting. She was way past the two--and-two welt, adding clickety inches with the rushing miles. Uncle James was asleep, his body swaying at the whim of the juddering express. His mouth had fallen slack, his glasses were perilously low on his nose, long fingers were locked across his waistcoated, watch-chained stomach. Above him was a dull photograph of Exmouth, and the luggage-laden rack.

Flora pressed her nose against the grimed window; the brim of her panama banged against the glass, so she pulled off the hat and dangled it by its chin-elastic. Power lines swooped as the train passed, to be jerked upwards by each pole — like naughty children by a parent's hand. A Shire mare and her foal cantered to the distant edge of their pasture, terrified by the thundering, smoke-plumed monster that disturbed their peaceful grazing.

Two men leaning on bikes, and a baker in his high green van, waited at a country crossing . . . village stations with rambler roses, shirt-sleeved porters and rows of milk churns were blurred, spurned by the speeding train.

A boy crossed a meadow behind a wandering herd of cows. At home, Father would be fetching their own cows for afternoon milking . . . Pansy and Bess, Roanie, Blackie and Flower. The glittering holiday lay ahead; but six-year-old Flora felt an uneasy twinge of homesickness, making the train-taste smokily bitter in her mouth. Auntie, seeing the near-crumpling face, laid down her needles in mid-row and pulled the pigtailed child to her knee, there to cuddle back the smiles . . .

"I spy!", she cheerfully began. "Nothing . . . " giggled Flora as the engine plunged, shrieking, into tunnel-darkness.

Eventually came a silver glimpse of sea. They panted into the familiar station, where Jonesie waved from the signal box and Porter Tom hoisted their cases on his flat truck, commenting embarrassingly upon the way that Flora had shot up since last summer.

The cobbled street sloped towards the harbour, so steeply that Flora's stamping feet threatened to run away, to carry her past the sharp turning to Staithe Street and straight over the wall where dozing boats rode the swelling tide. But she disciplined them in time. There, just as they had left it last year, was Sea Cottage with its whitewashed walls and geranium-packed window-boxes . . . and Mrs. Dickinson with arms widespread to catch her.

Mrs. Dickinson was square, the squarest little woman that Flora had ever seen. Short as short, she was wide in her black-and-white cotton dress. She wore black woollen stockings, even when the weather was sunburning hot, and a white sunbonnet framed her dear, smiling face. Mrs. Dickinson's husband was a fisherman who wore a thick blue jumper, and a special one for church on Sundays. Sometimes he sat outside the cottage door, quietly smoking a clay pipe and reading weather-messages in the clouds. But today he was in the garden at the back, busily planting a row of turnips.

Holiday Uncle was unrecognisable as Everyday Uncle who lived in a red-brick villa in town. Not that he really enjoyed the seaside, but Auntie gently bossed him into believing it was his duty and that it would set him up for the year. Meekly he always agreed that she was probably right.

Brown sea crept across the ribbed sand, waves curled into creamy foam then, spent, slithered coldly around Flora's small pink toes. Uncle's trousers were rolled almost to his knees, exposing thin white legs. He carried his shoes by their knotted laces as the sun bombarded his grey trilby and sparkled on the gold rims of his glasses. He smiled, momentarily lulled into forgetting that he was not enjoying himself. Auntie sat in in a hired deck-chair beside a seaweed-draped breakwater — a small cushion accommodated the nape of her neck. She sighed, letting her eyes wander contentedly over the huge bright sky and glinting sea. They saw five bored donkeys, with toddlers enthroned atop pommelled saddles, plodding through soft-dimpled sand. She had no meals to prepare, no pots to wash, a whole week during which no saffron duster must be propelled around the drawing-room furniture. Again she sighed and slept. She awoke reddened, quite sun-fuddled. Uncle had settled beside her in his own chair, good-naturedly allowing Flora to bury his elderly, misshapen feet.

Another small girl had been watching from where her own family had spread rugs and towels and bags. Now, warily, like two young animals, she and Flora drew together. Several hours later their friendship had borne a castle with turrets and paper flags and a moat filled, at Uncle's suggestion, by a trench connected to a pool. Auntie and Juliet's mother had talked themselves back into the delightful coincidence of a mutual girlhood in Sheffield and were nostalgically traversing the paths of "I remember".

The pier strode out on stilts. The revolving turn-

stile, itself exciting, released her into a promised wonder-
land. The decking boards drummed, hollow under all the
tramping feet. At first the beach was visible through the
cracks . . . soon there was sea, sucking and swirling at
the ironwork, oily dark in the shadows. Flora felt a
strange, fluttering butterfly of fear.

"Run on, lovey", Aunt suggested. But her legs were as
as another child's, unresponsive to her bidding. Once, at
home, Father had hoisted her up a ladder to the fragrant
top of a partly finished haystack; a hen had hurtled, cack-
ling, down into the rickyard, announcing that she had
left a warm brown egg for the finding. But at that small
height Flora had been seized by the same shivery dread
that now she felt. Gladly she turned, seeing the solid,
friendly town instead of the heaving grey horizon.

Uncle donned his black-speckled plimsolls one morning when a cool wind spitefully swept sand-flurries across the beach. With new cronies he happily padded the precious bowling green, then drank weak, tinned-milky tea in the pavilion.

Aunt Martha and Flora explored the shops, buying seaside rock, fondant pebbles and scallop shells filled with peppermints. Flora took her money from her clasp-topped purse to buy fat brown cigars in transparent tubes, one for Father and one for Uncle (to thank him for the holiday). For her little brother, who would be old enough to join them next year, she selected a wooden monkey that climbed a stick. From a revolving stand they chose postcards and went into a café away from the wind, to write them. Flora's fingers were sticky with cream that oozed from a meringue, so Auntie dipped a paper serviette in the hot-water jug and wiped them clean. Through the maw of the pillar box the cards thudded down inside — Flora knew that she could never fetch them back. Already they were away, one to the farm, three to her school friends and one that to-morrow would drop into the wire basket behind Gran's letter-box. And Gran would come singing from the kitchen, wiping her damp red hands on her apron — the corgi barking furiously meanwhile at the departed, now unattainable, postman.

Where the town hugged the harbour the sky screamed with gulls; fish waste was gorged before ever it hit the water. Fishermen mended their nets and lobster pots were piled in latticed, photogenic heaps. Uncle took his Box Brownie from its canvas case, recording the holiday for the grey pages of his album. A tall man in a striped swimming costume, a rubber cap fitting skin-tight on his head, dived from the jetty. He emerged triumphantly from the black depths with handfuls of plucked weed. Flora shuddered at the thought of that long lonely descent into the hazardous unknown.

Dusk was busy, loud, fun-filled. At home it would be moth-soft, with the barn owl hunting along the hedgerows and bat-squeaks scarcely audible in the yard. Cows would be grazing evening grass before dewfall. Mother, after tea, always took a bucket on her arm and went across the chicken paddock, pulling the growing pullets from under their huts and stowing them safely through the popholes, away from fox-harm. Perhaps Father would be with her . . . and Rover . . . and little Danny with his kite.

A slight trickle traversed Flora's cheek and reached her tongue, salty, sad. Auntie's arm reached out with a comforting squeeze. A small amusement arcade made a diversion, tempting with lights and entertainment. Flora watched as a crane descended into a trove of trashy prizes . . . it clenched and rose again, a packet of sweets precariously held in its fist. At its zenith it opened, perversely, teasingly. Again, unsuccessfully, Flora tried. Uncle took another penny from his pocket. . .

"Third time lucky, lassie . . . " he encouraged. Miraculously the crane held a china cat by one black leg . . . then lifted it slowly as suspense caught in Flora's throat and her wishing fingers were tightly crossed. Then, proving how wise was her Uncle (and how especially magical were lucky black cats with green glass eyes) the ornament dropped into the chute and into her welcoming, loving hands.

The salt on her lips was only the kiss of sea wind and happiness was bright in her eyes.

The Meeting

Miss Minnie was thrice-hampered. Her fingers, knobbled by rheumatism, stuck purplish from the knitted mitts that she always wore in winter; Parry's accompaniment to *"Jerusalem"*, note-spattered as a bun with currants, overbrimmed the simple vessel of her ability; lastly the temperamental piano, jangled by damp and neglect, had several dumb notes that added nothing but small confusing thuds to the music.

But twenty voices progressed with her through the hymn. Sam's Hilda provided a droning alto, rather flat, whilst Mrs. Lundy from the shop was richly tuneful with warbling emphasis on important notes. Mrs. Vicar, head flung back, exulted in the words, racing confidently ahead of Miss Minnie. She sped on to wield her bow of burning gold, finally, triumphantly (and probably single-handed) ensuring the building of Jerusalem in her particular corner of England's green and pleasant land.

Wall-hooks on the brown-painted partition near the Hut door held the Institute members' temporarily discarded coats — tweed, melton cloth or serviceable gaberdine. About them was an aroma of mothballs and damp dogs. Hats had remained on respective heads, from Miss Minnie's crocheted beret to Mrs. Vicar's perennial brown felt.

Mary from Glebe Cottage had carried six mince-pies for the competition, carefully packed in a square, flat basket. In her kitchen she had created the pastry that now, with flaky layers, cocooned the dark mincemeat, brandy-laced, that was well matured in her grey earthenware jars. The purchase of these had cost more hours than shillings at a cottage auction in a nearby village: now they were part of the traditional equipment for the new country living that she and Bill were enjoying so fully since their retirement. Bill had walked with her as far as the village, calling to spend a promised hour with old George who was unwillingly confined to bed with "one of his chests".

Actually there was nothing wrong, the old fellow grumpily insisted, that a good dollop of goose-grease wouldn't have cured. But Boss had been so perturbed by the laboured wheezing of each breath that he had brought him home in the trap. George, Boss knew, was becoming frail, each winter loosening slightly his fiercely white-knuckled grip on the fabric of familiar working life.

Bessie's pies, large, plump and sugar-sprinkled, had suffered on the journey across the fields — when they were, in fact, still warm and thus vulnerable to the jolting of her striding steps. The plate upon which they were now displayed was functional, though somewhat discoloured and oven-crazed. Anxiously, Polly fussed that *her* pies rested only on a paper doily, whereas Mrs. Joey's were separated by a filigree of starched white lace from a gold-garlanded china plate. "Don't fret, luv. It's only the grub they're judging", Bessie reassured her. "Nobody ever ate a plate, nor a doily neither, come to think of it!"

Bessie was quite content with her mince-pies. No matter what the judge decided, no matter the opinion of everybody in the whole village — her Bert had always reckoned they couldn't be beaten. She could see him now, prising off the lids with a knife and inserting a goodly lump of her home-made cheese. Each meant, he said, a "happy month" to the eater and he cheerfully made sure of his year-long quota.

The slithering and clattering of chairs on the wooden floor prefaced an outbreak of chatter. Miss Minnie vacated the piano stool and took a chair on the second row. The tortoise stove glowed hotly, so hotly that Sybil, the President, removed her cardigan. She laid it over the back of her chair, where it drooped, fawn and shapeless. Sybil was thin as a lath and the cardigan cushioned the contact between hard chair and her bony body. She clapped her hands for attention. Mrs. Lundy finished her conversation (and several whispered afterthoughts) before Sybil cleared her throat and announced the Roll Call. This was to be "My Best Christmas Present". From childhood Maisie remembered a bright yellow teddy bear that had materialised on her bedside table in the silver moonlight of a cold Christmas dawning. She had, she mused, still less than wakeful, left her lumpy stocking till later. Pulling the teddy into bed, warmth and sleep had engulfed them both.

Sally and Jenny from Standard One had proudly carried the schoolchildren's present across the lane to Auntie's cottage. It was a cyclamen plant with pale pink blooms, wrapped in green paper from the florist's shop in town. All through January and February it had flowered, each pointed bud growing above the beautiful leaves then unfurling into exquisite petals. Under Auntie's special loving care it had lived through many seasons, spending summers on the peaty border beneath the larder window — being brought indoors before the time of frost. Now again it stood on Auntie's sideboard in the blue, swirly patterned jardinière. Someone had, last year, received a soft and luxurious pair of fur-lined gloves and Sybil's favourite gift was a pretty silver thimble for her collection.

The demonstrator was young and slim, in a white

overall and with a white band controlling her wavy fair hair. Mrs. Dan, mouth turned down at the corners, fingers supporting her chin, and thumb making another pucker in a walnut-wrinkled face, was not suited. What, she thought, were things coming to? She herself (and most of the others now awaiting the demonstration) had been icing cakes before this slip of a flighty girl had even been thought of. Mrs. Dan had left her fire thriftily "backed up" for the afternoon with a shovelful of slack well dampened with tea-leaves. Dan would be dozing now, eyes closed in fitful sleep against the gloomy room. She hoped the embroidered antimacassar would not be crumpled . . . if she were there she could tweak it from harm, and he, awakened, would look at her with reproachful spaniel-eyes.

"Hullo, ladies", began the girl. Her dismay as Mrs. Dan's sniffish glance pierced her youthful confidence was quickly dispelled by the welcoming applause led by the President — and the smiling face of Mrs. Vicar encouraging her from the front row. With skill freshly learned at Domestic Science College, Jilly shared her knowledge of the intricacies of icing. Rosettes and flowers, lattice-work and shells clothed her ready marzipan'd cake and even Mrs. Lundy was silent as she watched. Perhaps she would need to order some extra icing sugar and maybe a few more colourings beside the usual cochineal? Despite herself, even Mrs. Dan considered doing something a bit more ambitious with the cake (economy recipe) that was stored away at home.

Ruth's chilblains itched inside her snow-boots — "Rub them with an onion dipped in salt", advised Miss Minnie as together they drank their tea. The afternoon provided an enjoyable pause in the Christmas rush, unaccustomed leisure to sip instead of gulping. Bessie's arrowroot biscuits were unashamedly dunked — there were some (like the housekeeper from the Hall) who crooked their little fingers and tried to be "posh" — but only succeeded,

Bessie thought, in looking foolish.

The Secretary fussed after Jilly, who was awarding marks for the competition. Joking that she would surely grow fat, (and kindly warned of the bad luck to follow if she cut a mince-pie) she broke a taste-sized piece from each entry. Hilda's were, she decided, completely faultless. Three more points were added to a total that, by March, would bring to Hilda the cup that she had already won for five successive years.

Late afternoon was dark beyond the opened door of the Hut. Packed into her little car with all her paraphernalia (and Hilda's mince-pies for her tea) Jilly waved as she chugged away down the lane. Lamplight came from the Smithy and Liz was barrowing mangolds to the ewes — thin snow was darkened by the flock's hoof-tracks across the yard. Her mother trod a studied way along the comparative dryness of the sheltered path by the barn. Mindless of the possible fate of her best shoes she hurried excitedly to see the newest lambs, birth-slimed and wallowing in their warm-strawed pen.

Bessie hauled her bike from against the hedge and switched on her lights — Hilda walked with her to the corner of the lane.

Mrs. Dan, entering the kitchen, immediately noticed that Dan had thoughtfully removed and folded the freshly-ironed antimacassar before taking his afternoon rest. He watched her as she stirred the fire, glad when at last the thick swirls of yellow smoke brought forth hesitant flames and then a roaring blaze. He was surprised when, in a rare expression of affection, his wife smiled at him as she pulled the skewering pin from her hair, thus releasing her hat.

Country Wedding

L ime trees were summer-thick; pale leaves fluttered in the kindly breeze that relieved the heat of the dingy street. The houses that they shaded, once gracious, were now forlorn. Their spaciousness had been divided into bed-sitting-rooms and flats, into drab little worlds of gas rings, primus stoves and worn, brown lino. Paintwork was faded and flaked, doors were pockmarked by long-popped blisters; dust and crumpled paper drifted into corners by tradesmen's entrances that now gaped on broken hinges. Joyce pulled the fourth bell, pushed open the door and climbed the naked, creaking stairs.

A dressmaker's dummy, a mahogany knob for its head, and three mahogany feet for support, commanded the gloomy landing. Its pouting bust and generous hips curved from its nipped, once-fashionable Edwardian waist. Joyce sidled past and knocked on a nearby door.

Madame Olivia was large and sagging; her mauve jumper had collected stains from the tea that always dripped when she lifted the cup from a carelessly-slopped saucer. Her pilled green cardigan bore a battalion of pins, her grey skirt was seated and shiny and her troublesome feet lived gratefully in capacious tartan slippers.

Garments, just begun, were piled on the table; materials temporarily joined by lines of white tacking hung over chairs and her treadle sewing-machine reigned in a corner. Joyce's two-piece, ready for collection, hung from the picture-rail. Perhaps the pink flowers on its blue silken surface were just a bit larger and brighter than they looked on the roll of material? But Madame Olivia assured her, as she tweaked and patted it onto Joyce's thin figure, that it certainly was exactly right for someone as important as the Bride's Mother!

Joyce walked to the Market Square to catch Joey's 'bus — one more job crossed from a long, long list.

Polly left the vestry door wide open. The water-butt was in the grey angle of the church wall and even on a bright summer day the child needed the reassurance of voices and laughter at her back. Quickly she dipped the greenish water; it was specked with floating gnats and moths that never again would gyrate in the heat nor fly in the owl-haunted night. She felt watched by those leaning, ivy-twined gravestones; perhaps something lurked, leering, behind iron railings that surrounded a weather-smeared marble vault. She ran back with her splashing can, closing the door firmly on the eerie long-grassed graveyard.

The Vicar's wife stood on a chair, whilst Mother handed up fragrant phlox and damp delphiniums to transform the ugly brass vase that stood in the deep window with the glowing ruby glass. William pulled off his tweed cap as he carried in an armful of carnations from the Manor greenhouse. They were bridal white, haughty, aloof — Polly preferred the friendlier flowers that she had helped to gather from this early morning's garden. A thrush had sung as she worked and drops from last night's thunderstorm had spattered from wet leaves to her brown arms and gingham dress. Now she followed Mrs. Vicar, treading reverently and sandal-softly, on the red carpet that led to the altar — her voice was suitably tuned to a whisper.

Soon the flowers were placed, icy, perfect, fern-flounced in the narrow-necked silver vases. Dark, carved oak made a sombre background — but sunshine beamed through the East window, through the Madonna's sapphire robe and the lovely radiance of her halo. The little Christ Child held out a chubby hand, seeming to smile directly at the flowers.

Old George sat on a milking stool in the harness-room doorway. Reins were ribbon-supple as they passed from hand to knobbled hand. Every piece of leather had the sheen of new chestnuts; each brass ornament, buckle and stud gleamed like pure gold. The trap was covered by the small rick sheet, lest white fantails should sully the smartly varnished coachwork as they flew from cowshed to barn roof and then back again to preen and croon on the pigsty wall. Taffy, already groomed, was dozing in the shadowed stable, his hooves occasionally scraping on the brick floor.

Later, George would back the pony between the graceful shafts, giving the dappled coat a last rub down with a cloth and adjusting the harness. Then he would proudly lead the outfit round to the house, and Gaffer and the Mrs. would bring out the newly-ironed white ribbons.

Bessie busily washed and dried the crockery from the Village Hall cupboard, filling the trays for Mary to carry away. Apron'd helpers scurried noisily about the wooden floor, covering damask-cloth'd trestles with piled sandwiches, dishes of fancies, and buttered currant loaf. Square tins, round tins and covered baskets emptied their mince pies, their golden-crusted sausage-rolls, their cheesecakes and shortbreads. Joyce counted and worried and wondered, but Bessie calmed her with the truth that there was sure to be more than enough and probably a good deal to spare. Smilax trailed among plates and sparkling glasses; sweet peas in ornate and contorted epergnes were able to over-perfume the fusty smell that somehow always pervaded the Hall.

Cook from the Manor admired the three-tier cake, arranged to her instructions on its silver-plated stand. It was black and rich, moist as pudding, matured for six months and then wrapped in almond paste and dressed in royal icing. With swags and swirls she had decorated it, her hands dry, and nose and throat filled with seeping sweetness of sieved and billowing sugar. Silver bells and horseshoes had completed the task, one traditionally entrusted to her each time there was a wedding on the Estate.

The Vicar stood at his study window. Faded pink roses peeped in at him and shabby careworn starlings, grub-laden, flew constantly to their demanding broods under the eaves. Theo, the long-haired cat, sprawled in the shade of the hedge, teasing at and nibbling a spread front paw. Vicar remembered Lilian's christening and, to his dismay and slight disbelief, her Father's too. Country years had passed quietly, their pace ever swifter as his own pink head grew balder and his sparse hair whiter. In happy times and sorrow, at great events and throughout the humdrum everydays, he had shepherded and cared for his flock. Now he smiled, knelt by a leather chair to offer his customary prayer and then reached for his starched surplice; he took a prayer book from its drawer and walked across the garden and through the yew arch to the Church.

Old Mr. Biggs was failing. But his daughter had set a chair outside the door, helped him gently into it and wrapped a rug round his knees. She had picked a red rosebud and pinned it to the front of his cardigan, just clear of the bushy grey beard. Living in the cottage near the lychgate he had missed hardly a wedding. Lilian would wave to him, he knew, as she drove to Church with her Father in the trap.

Lucy stood on tiptoes in her new black pumps with the criss-crossed elastic — she twirled and craned, then ques-

30

tioned the reason for Mavis's restraining hand in its lacy white mitten. Lucy had no mittens, but her green satin dress was as beautiful and as grown-up looking as Mavis's. She sniffed at her posy of yellow roses; they tickled her nose and a loud sneeze almost dislodged the circlet of artificial daisies pinned to her hair.

Harry and Shep, with Arthur from the shop, stood just inside the belfrey door — after the service they would send out a peal so joyous that it would sound all over the surrounding fields and hills, into every cottage and almost to the market town. Eight choirboys and two men rustled the leaves of their hymn-books. Joyce, in her Madame Olivia two-piece (now crowned by a blue straw and embellished by a corsage) rummaged with glove-cumbered hands for an embroidered handkerchief from her bag. She looked across the aisle at Bob and his Best Man, who sat very upright in their navy serge suits. Their hair was bleached by the sun and the backs of their necks ruddy from haymaking days that had only just been completed. Bob was a good lad and Joyce was thankful that he was taking her Lilian no further than the next village.

The congregation shuffled and murmured. Bill, the Churchwarden, signalled to Miss Minnie who coaxed the harmonium to a crescendo of its wheezing best — everyone was too excited to bother about any missed notes. Dressed in his high-buttoned tweed, Herbie led his daughter into the Church. Mary smoothed the white satin gown and gently pushed Lucy into place beside Mavis. Lilian's auburn hair was Eugène-frizzed under her veil, namesake flowers showered from her hands.

To Miss Minnie's triumphal bars the Bride and her Father walked together down the aisle. Joyce pressed the embroidered hanky quickly to her eyes.

The Album

Stiff pages of creamy-coloured card were imprisoned, gilt-edged, within embossed brown covers . . . covers securely closed by a brass-furnish'd clasp. Only by reaching tiptoe-tall could Monica ease it from the bookcase shelf where it lived with rows of musty, dark-bound volumes that nobody ever read.

She scurried from the quiet room, glad when the door was closed behind her, then sped along the tiled hall, through the draught curtain that momentarily wrapped her in dusty folds of red plush; pantingly she reached the warm safety of the kitchen.

Great-Aunt Elspeth sat in the cushioned Windsor chair, a rumbling cat on her lap and her work-box within finger-reach. Aunt Elspeth had a complaint — something that made her sit for long hours in her chair, that prevented her from going for walks or working in the garden. With her complaint she could never cycle down Thorny Lane and catch the 'bus to town, as Granny had done to-day, but would eagerly await her sister's return with the shopping and a whole evening's worth of news.

To-day Aunt was mending, the mushroom'd sock gaining a beautiful darn as the long needle wove meticulously under and over. But readily her work was laid aside, old Ginger gently transferred to the hearth-rug, when Monica placed the album on her knee and settled on the tapestry stool at her feet.

Monica's Granny was dumpy and small; she dressed in misty blues that matched her eyes, eyes that were magnified by thick shiny lenses in gold-rimmed spectacles. But Aunt Elspeth's Grandmamma had a thin face with a long thin nose, bright little bird-eyes. She didn't look, Monica mused, as though she ever smiled or bestowed a warm kiss and loving hug in passing as Granny often did. This sepia-brown Grandmamma was seated on a high-backed chair, long black skirt covering her shoes and a ribbon'd black cap on her smooth, centre-parted hair; she looked stern, almost terrifying. Her elbow rested on a cane table which also held a dreary aspidistra and a Bible.

"She had a hard life, dearie", Aunt Elspeth's voice was soft. "Grandpapa went early into a decline and died quite young, leaving poor Grandmamma with four children to rear. I remember her getting up in the early mornings to clean her house, then working at gown and mantle-making till the dwindling of day and far beyond. There was always someone calling for a fitting and Grandmamma would kneel on the floor, pins bristling her lips, as her client twirled slowly around, reflected in the cheval-glass and ready to criticise the set of a flounce or the line of a hem."

Monica saw anew the small pressed-tight mouth, the drawn face lined from working into the night with only an oil-lamp to light the path of tiny stitches, to illuminate the ranks of tucks and patterns of jet and steel beads. Great-Grandmamma must have had little to make her smile . . .

Another Great-Grandma . . . ("from the other side of the family, dearie") stood meekly, dutifully, by her seated husband, her body moulded by her stays and several chins resting on the high neckline of her dress. She had lived with Aunt Elspeth's parents for the last ten widow'd years of her life. She kept her money in a drawstring'd suede bag, secreted in the deep pocket of her dress. Picking out a halfpenny or even, rarely, a whole

TE—C

penny, she would send one of her grandchildren to Mrs. Lewin's parlour-shop for sweets.

"Have you eaten any?" the old lady would enquire from the returning child who stood hopefully, expectantly and still breathlessly at her side. Upon being assured that not one fragment of cinder toffee, not one aniseed ball or acid drop was missing, she would stow away the pointed packets with her purse. "That's a good child . . ." Then Grandmamma would contentedly bulge her cheek with a selected goodie, smug in her selfishness.

"Poor Mother!" Aunt Elspeth sighed. "She must have had a dreadful time with her. You see, Monica, she never forgave Mother for marrying her only son and showed it right up to the day she died. Once, Mother had taken some jam tarts from the kitchen range. Closing the oven door she was in danger of burning her fingers on the hot metal, so popped the twelve-tin momentarily on the hearth-rug.

"Grandma contrived to step clumsily right into the middle. I shall never forget Mother's anguished cry . . . *'Oh, Grandma! You did that on purpose!'* That was the only time I saw anyone go into screaming hysterics . . . Mother fled upstairs with thumping, stumbling, tear-blinded steps and we amazed children were left to scrape raspberry jam from Grandma's felt slippers, whilst she muttered and chuntered about people who allowed their feelings to run out of control.

"At family mealtimes we sat at the dinning table, which was always covered with a crisp damask cloth. Grandma ate quickly, eyes on the joint or the last wedge of steamed pudding. 'A little more, Grandma?' — 'No, dear. Let the children have it,' the old lady would reply as she presented her wiped-clean plate for the last roast potato or another slice of beef.

"I'll tell you another thing that happened. Mother had made one of her special apple batters. I had been saving until last the crispest, most sugary morsel. 'Why is

Elspeth pushing that piece about her plate in that ill-mannered way?' Grandma enquired. 'Little girls that don't know what's good should be taught a lesson!' And her big shining fork swooped like a marauding bird, took up the tit-bit and popped it greedily into her own mouth.

"Great Uncle Bertie was a gamekeeper, many years ago when Squire was a little boy and his Father kept a large staff. There were splendid shoots, and days and days of preparations beforehand, with the cooking of turkeys and hams and great crusted pies. Uncle Bertie was also a taxidermist and had a wonderful collection; there were jays and stoats and even a vixen's mask. But I don't know what happened to them, except for the squirrel in the dining-room."

Monica, secretly, avoided the squirrel. There it was, forever captured on a piece of grey-lichen'd branch . . . its tufted ears were unhearing, its dainty paws clasped a nut that never would be eaten. Never again would its bushy tail stream handsomely behind as it bounded, chattering, up the beech trees.

Uncle Bertie had apprehended a poacher one dark woodland night. Old Squire had rewarded him with a sovereign, but the encounter had cost Bertie two fingers of his left hand.

Among the pages, between curly-haired two-year-old Grandpa, (black-clad in uncomprehending mourning for his father) and seventeen-year-old Lily with her handspan waist and large feather-trimmed hat, was an empty space. The mount was viciously torn as though emptied in anger or with welling hatred.

"Don't ask about that page, child, for I can't really tell you . . ." Aunt shook her head sadly, gazing with eyes that maybe hoped to summon the moustached, arrogant face of the youth who had reputedly behaved so disgracefully that his person had departed across the world and his image been removed and burnt; thus his very existence had been suitably wiped from the lives of outraged Victorian parents.

Somewhere upstairs the gusting wind rattled a door. "Just go and make sure the apple room door is latched", Aunt Elspeth asked, perhaps thoughtlessly. "Well, take Ginger with you for company!" she coaxed, when the child nervously shook her head . . . "and I'll stand here at the bottom of the stairs and wait for you".

The cat bounded ahead, around the corner, and then stopped to rub luxuriously, purring, against the bannister rails. Monica followed more slowly and Aunt Elspeth stood, supported by her walking-stick, tunelessly singing *Rule Britannia* to encourage the little girl on her way.

"Bring my jewel box down now, dearie, and I'll show you something," she called as Monica reappeared.

In the red leather box, with its velvet-lined tray, lay a silver brooch engraved with twining flowers wreathing a blue-enamell'd bird. "Now, child, see if you can find that brooch in the album". She guided the excited hand as it turned the pages. At last they reached a very old lady with spaniel-eared cap. Minnie had died in her ninety-ninth year and there, at her throat, nestling on white lace was the brooch that presently gleamed in Monica's palm.

"She was your Great-Grandmother's sister", explained Aunt, who had always been an authority on family history. "That brooch has been handed down through generations and I think it is just right for a little girl that I know to wear on Sundays . . ."

Tenderly she closed Monica's fingers over the treasure and the delighted child cuddled close.

Summertime

Dying elms, ivy-strangled, were teased by the raucous rabble of raggedy rooks. Ungainly birds strutted on the twig-strewn path, or vaulted upon leaning headstones where forgotten names were finally obliterated by spreading lichens of golden-orange and silver-green. The hedge seethed with a noisy gang of sparrows, summer-shabby parents and their fawn-fluffed youngsters. A starling glinted purple, then bronze, as he was pursued by four petulant, slant-eyed adolescents.

Hay, fragrant as tobacco in the sun, was stacked bale upon greenish bale in the Church Farm barns; a ginger cat walked across an empty trailer, then leapt, a tiger, into dead-nettles and jungled hemlock. A neat grey bantam progressed slowly down the garden, diligently scratching, then summoning her brood to see what she had found. They, as though on wheels, scurried about her — three balls of honey-puff, two black and two brown. Delicately the hen picked a crannied spider from a blue brick. A brown chick leapt to win it from her beak, then scuttled with his prize to the protection of a monstrous lettuce.

Red bullocks grazed the Hill Field, swishing tails and tossing back their heads to ease the burden of biting, clustering flies. An old roan pony, one hind-leg at rest and grizzled head drooping, drowsed in the huge shadow of a kindly chestnut tree. Towards him, saddle over her arm and bridle trailing, apple in her pocket and terrier at heel, came a sunburnt child with jutting plaits. The pony roused himself as Jenny approached, shuffled towards

37

her and nuzzled her pocket before taking the apple with gentle mouth from her outstretched palm. Jenny pressed her cheek against the familiar head and listened as yellow teeth crunched the fruit. Then she placed the saddle on the pony's back, reached under the hot round belly and fastened the girths while her head supported the saddle flaps with their intermingled scents of leather and horse.

Mouth now free of apple the pony accepted the bit, champing it in place as the girl slipped the headband behind his ears, hooking free his forelock with a flick of her finger. Swinging herself into place she patted and coaxed him forward, her heels urging him to the shambling semi-trot that had long replaced the cavortings of his youth. The terrier escort raced ahead.

In the Glebe, hurdled pens were crammed with sheep, bleating, uneasy and disturbed. Ewes were still white from clipping, but lambs looked grey by comparison in four-month growth of fleece. Jess lay against the hedge, cool on a patch of bare brown earth; her chin rested on the ground but eyes were alert and a white-tasselled tail brushed the dust in welcome. Jack, the young dog, crept on his stomach around the pens, curling his lip and snapping as ewes butted their heads against the wood, defiantly stamping at the collie. Ben shouted to "Lie down, dam' you!" Jack cowered, humiliated, but soon returned, over-tempted, to his delinquency.

The sheep bunched and huddled and Jenny slid from the pony and squatted beside the dogs. She stroked Jack's smooth black-and-white head, scratched him behind his silken ears. Jess jealously pushed closer to be noticed and Flip the terrier bounced into the group, sending the child rolling, laughing, off-balance on the grass.

Father stood by the gate, straightening his aching back; Shep whistled softly to Jess and Jack, and prepared to open the first pen. The strong disinfectant smell was all about, perhaps twenty sodden-fleeced, dripping sheep shook their heads, black ears flapping wetly.

Jenny watched as the last batch went through the dip tank. Joe caught and hauled each protesting animal in turn, treading precariously on ground awash with muck and water. Each ludicrous dance ended with the sheep slurping into the bath, droplets of yellowish spray flying into the sunlit air. Father pushed and propelled with his dipping iron, then allowed his affronted victim to climb the escape ramp and rush, offended, to rejoin the flock.

Parson walked through the yew arch that opened from his garden into the churchyard. Last night's scything party had laid the dense froth of hedge parsley and swathes were already crisping in the heat. The bottom of his cassock was soon powdered with white dust from the drying flowers. He glanced upwards at the weather-cock that stood motionless, gilded, against a sky that was blue like speedwells or the Siamese kitten's eyes. The heavy door groaned as he pushed it open, the Church was cool and sequestered, dim save where the sun looked through stained-glass windows and puddled jewel colours on flagstoned aisles in grey, venerable walls.

In the spinney, summer hummed with gyrating gnats, buzzed with flies that fumbled among the bramble flowers. Clumsy bees worked the willow-herb and the loosestrife; a wood-pigeon burst from a hazel bush, one small smoky feather drifting to earth from urgent, applauding wings. A weasel crossed from a clump of nettles, rippled over emerald moss on a tree stump and dropped into embracing wilderness.

Polly walked the clovered verge between her cottage and the small red letter-box. She posted her letter, then went up the path between regimented salvias that stood so proudly in disciplined ranks of Post Office scarlet. She was grateful for the shade of her old straw hat, for afternoon sun was hot at her back. The cacophonous bell jangled on its spring, announcing that she had arrived to collect her pension.

□

Albert

Albert sat at his kitchen table. A lump of yellowed, singing Stilton was hacked to join broken pieces of the heel of a stale loaf. So, absent-mindedly, he nourished his body. His eyes followed a piloting finger along the lines of sale notices in the *Advertiser*: thus he fed his mind. The pint mug at his elbow held steaming tea, the black strength turned rusty, turgid, by swirls of Guernsey cream. This week's paper, digested along with his fill-belly, would add yet another layer to weeks and months of local news; somewhere far beneath was hidden a deal table top with its original covering of brown American cloth. A hurricane lamp stood on an upturned biscuit tin lid. On dark evenings it had cast lurching light as Albert walked about yard and byre. Later it fought the shadowy gloom of the vast, stark and stone-flagged kitchen. Now, unlit and resting, it wept paraffin into the lid — its reek mingled with those of fustiness, reesty bacon, farmyard coats and the cheese.

His life, though apparently austere and comfortless, nevertheless suited the dealer well. He ate sufficiently, if without refinement; the waggoner's wife washed and mended for him and often brought him a batch of scones or some sausage rolls. But his mother (God rest her) had hoped to see him contentedly married to a good wife who would look after him as she herself had always done — keeping the larder filled with bread and fruit cakes, its shelves laden with chutneys and jam. She had prayed for a daughter-in-law to churn the butter and dress the poultry, to see that her only son never sat about in wet clothes, nor wanted for hand-knitted socks, loyal companionship, nor his favourite baked suet puddings. His mother would have been saddened to find Albert wifeless still, the drawing-room cobwebbed and cold, its curtains rotting into tatters as they hung; she would probably have cried to walk into a dining-room so silent and deserted, where her lace-edged and embroidered tablecloths slept, folded, in the drawers, her silver tea-service was tarnished in the sideboard and the bobble-fringed red chenille cover lay grey with dust on the long mahogany table. Only the kitchen, and Albert's bedroom with its flaking ceiling and narrow iron bed, together with the dark landing and back staircase that connected them, ever knew footfall in the old, brooding house.

Albert was so thin that the ritual of his dressing included the wrapping, puttee-wise, of a strip of cloth from knee to ankle, thus adequately padding the chestnut-shiny leggings. A steel hook wrenched each button through its own buttonhole and a yellow duster gave final polish to the gleaming boots, so long and narrow that the toes rose slightly from the ground.

Snuff taken from an ebony, silver-mounted box produced, predictably, a massive sneeze that was collected in a khaki handkerchief. Albert looked happily through the soap-spattered window to the garden beyond. One of his deals had brought him a sack of daffodil bulbs as "luck" from a grateful client well pleased with a bunch of promising young steers. Albert, delighted, had spent three September evenings excavating divots from rough grass with a broken steel knife, then settling the treasure deeply into fibrous earth. Now this glad April day, rain-washed, was golden-clumped by their flowering. Blue-green spears, defying winter, had come thrusting forth — then youthful green buds had appeared, turned to point downwards and finally opened into a wealth of brazen, splendid blooms.

All these stages Albert had watched as he sharpened his cut-throat on the strop that hung beside the sink, as he lathered his chin with a badger hair brush or as, methodically, he washed the few dirty crocks produced by each meal. Soon he must take the tins of saved seed from the dresser cupboard, sort the purple-dappled beans and crinkled marrowfat peas. Beetroot and lettuce, onion and carrot, he would buy from the seedsman whose dusty-dim shop was but a step from the cattle-market gate. There Seth, a gnarled little man in a hessian apron, haggled happily with his regulars, spreading balm of a few pence discount thinly over lengthy chat, plodding thuddingly about on his boarded floor, dipping a scoop into this or that rolled sack — grass seed all shiny-fine, or fertiliser of nose-wrinkling malodour.

There had been a note crannied in Albert's gatepost this morning. Jimmy, late for school, had left it there on passing. Dick, over the hill, had a calf to sell. Albert mounted his bike, pedalling hasteless along the lane. Cool violets grew secretly in the depths of the greening hedge; spring was whispering, fragrant and damp. Albert dismounted, leaned his bike against the post and his elbows on the top rail of the gate. Two horses, manes and fetlocks tossing in the breeze, harness jangling, breasted steadily towards him. Dick reined them in, coming from behind the drill to talk awhile. Rooks scavenged over disturbed earth and the horses rested quietly on the headland. Grey-woollen matrons, busy-mouthed, grazed and bleated in Copse Close — baby-voiced lambs gambolled in groups, then rushed in hunger to waiting dams.

"Good sheep, those," commented Albert. "I didn't hurt you over that bit of business".

"No," admitted Dick, "they don't owe me a lot. There's been a good fall of lambs and they've never looked back."

The bawling orphan calf filled the echoing loose box with its urgent cries — its dark red coat had dried crisply, unlicked by loving mother-tongue. Its violet-dark eyes seemed unfocusing as it staggered towards possible sustenance, froth-marking doorpost and wall and butting at Albert's hand, fisted atop his stick.

"Not a bad calf — plenty of bone. I'll bid you once and you can take it or leave it." Half an hour saw the difference split, with a deal struck somewhere between Dick's asking price and Albert's parrying bid. Hands were clasped, notes exchanged and Albert urged his bike towards home, with half-a-crown luck-money stowed in the draw-string bag in which he kept his change.

Where the Common met Dirty Lane, a chubby man with jacket snugly tied with band about his waist and cord trousers similarly held about his ankles was cleaning the runnels that traversed the grass verges. Winter's hands had gradually blocked them with debris and gravel from frost-crumbled road — with shovel, spade and brush Humph cleared them again for their purpose of draining surface water to the hedgeside ditch. From passer-by to the roadman and on to next passer-by; from market town and farm; to shop, blacksmith and cottage; on wheels, on horseback or on pairs of striding country feet, news and information was circulated. Fact, rumour, speculation or hearsay was processed under the mis-shapen balaclava that Humph wore year-long, then per-petuated by words that came tumbling from beneath the

43

shaggy eaves of his unkempt moustache. Albert learnt that Bessie's cow had calved and had ample milk to rear another youngster along with her own.

In the strawed cart (covered for safety by a net) and pulled by Blossom, the calf rode, still bawling, across the fields. Yearling cattle, newly turned out to grass in the young year, cavorted in escort. They were disturbed by the stirring calls of the calf, half-fearful of the rumbling cart, the great grey mare and Albert the charioteer, who waved his whip and shouted to clear them from his path.

Between the instinctive efforts of the fostering roan cow to repulse him, encouraged by Bessie, guided and shoved by Albert, the interloper took the first meal of his adopted life — enough to soothe his hunger and quieten his yearning cries. Installed behind the pen-hurdle that Bessie had fixed across the shed corner, milky-mouth nuzzled milky-mouth as the two calves became acquainted.

Liver and onions came hot to the table, with mashed potatoes white-mounded. Gravy thickened in the pan, bubbling gently within the stirring-wake of Bessie's spoon. Albert scraped up a chair, reaching for the knife and fork placed ready for him on the gingham cloth.

'Miss'

Miss Catharine still enjoyed winter, although she now found that her comfort needed more organisation. Even her stone hot-water bottle, in the flannelette-lined nest between goose-feather bed and woollen blankets, could not insulate her from the icy air in her bedroom. So she piled embroidered cushions into her winged and squashy armchair in the parlour and drew up a padded stool for her feet. "After all," she said conspiratorially to herself and to Caesar, the long-haired tabby, "nobody will ever know!"

With a large lump of coal placed flat upon her evening's fire and a basketful of Harry's ash logs against the hearth; with thick velvet curtains tightly drawn and a draught-excluding sausage lying at the door, she could sigh with cosy contentment. She was soothed by the ticking clock, lulled by Caesar's rumbling, purring dreams. Gentle firelight danced on the ceiling, smiled at her from the front of the mahogany sideboard. The fire itself murmured with small rustles and cracklings, moved and lived with imagined pictures and shapes that changed like a kaleidoscope when spent pieces of wood crumbled to red ash. Sparks darted, glowing, on the chimney's black throat, fireflies among the soot.

Frequently she awoke during the night. Then it amused her to think of her nieces and nephews . . . "Fancy!" they would probably say. "She's sleeping all night in a chair . . . and with an open fire of all things! It's time something was done . . . should be in a Home at her age!" But they were safely miles away, distantly sleeping in modern flats stacked beside main roads in the great impersonal, uncaring city. She was in her cottage in a friendly village, her snow-wrapped garden in front and Twelve-Acre Close behind, white-sparkled beneath a frost-moon and a myriad stars. They heard the incessant roar of night-traffic; she knew only the hoot of a barn owl and, at dawn, the crowing of a bantam at the farm.

Usually Miss Catherine's accumulating years annoyed her. She knew that never again would she go to France, nor to Denmark, nor delightedly to Rome. Her long school holidays had been spent in absorbing history, studying and learning. She had visited churches and castles, delved into museums, enquired and wondered and searched. Pamphlets and leaflets were kept between the pages of her many books, pencilled notes in her clear, bold handwriting brimmed the margins, overflowed in enthusiasm, comment or honestly in disagreement.

Now she could not climb the stile and ramble through the woods, nor sit on the hillside grass in summer to gaze upon the countryside spread all around her, patched with brown and gold and green. The horizon on clear days still wore a shimmer of grey sea, but she saw only the gulls that came screaming inland to scavenge behind the plough. Disciplined in her old age she would physically shake off her self-pity, chiding herself and curtly bidding herself to be thankful.

Defiantly, after such a mood, Miss Catherine would lift her mac from its peg in the hall, zip on her lined boots and drag her soft felt hat firmly down with both hands — with a knitted scarf wrapped round her neck she would march off to the village shop, an umbrella giving her confidence and support. Lately, though she had discussed the matter with none but herself, brief attacks of dizziness bothered her. However, she scorned the use of a walking-stick. Once have it "tittle-tattled" round the village that she was "failing" and people would start bringing her jugs of soup!

Miss Catherine, as a newly-qualified teacher, had needed to reinforce the frailty of a diminutive body with an assumed armour of severity. All of the boys (and a few girls) in Standard I could look down on top of her head with its coiled plait; clumping country-studded boots that scraped on the floor were monstrous beside her size four shoes with the pretty buttons; capable hands that smudged the books and carried coal for the schoolroom fire, made her own fingers appear daintier by comparison.

"Our teacher," wrote Hilda when seven, "will not let us put our hands in our pockets when it is cold". Maybe, because of belief instilled during her own childhood that only idle hands rested in aprons or trousers, she was unintentionally forgetful of draughty corners of the class-room furthest from the fire, where fingers were made white by cold, too numbed to guide a pencil. One day she had closed Willie Green's pockets with large stitches of double thread; even Dan of the expletive-rich vocabulary kept careful control of his tongue when, nowadays, he worked in her garden. Forty years had not lessened the memory-taste of carbolic soap with which she had forced him to cleanse his mouth at the pump!

Every third year Harry repainted the outside of the cottage. He never asked about the colour, just took round the usual amounts of dark brown and cream. "It looks business-like," Miss Catherine told him, " . . . and it lasts so much better than all those fancy colours they use today". When Harry prepared his bill it was as though he still expected a red tick, or even an angry cross and the red comment *"Disgraceful!"* Carefully he looped and formed his letters, lined his figures in neat columns and checked his reckoning, percentage discount and spelling. A spatter of ink from his thin nib or a smear from an anxious hand would send him for another sheet of paper . . . "Try, try again!" Miss Catherine had admonished her pupils all that long time ago.

A yellow piano, with curly brass candlesticks and fretted front backed with pink silk, sat across the corner in the parlour. The stool held books of nursery rhymes, bound copies of familiar classics and the *Ancient and Modern* hymn book that had joined her to open and close each school day. There were songs that had been laboriously taught to school choirs for concerts . . . and there were carols.

Maudie, the Home Help, was peeling potatoes in the kitchen when she heard the opening notes of *"Silent Night"*. She walked through and together they sang the lovely words. Then drying her hands on her apron she put an arm round the thin shoulders of her old teacher . . . and impulsively kissed the tear-damp cheek.

Colin Carr

Miss Myrtle and Miss Patience

Miss Myrtle was morning-busy. With her check duster she flicked and polished. Obsessively she blew into corners to dislodge invisible dust; finicking she moved and tweaked and re-arranged, patting the haberdashery into place and disciplining loose ends of narrow lace and ric-rac braid. She wore a plum-purple dress, a mauve modesty vest pinned into its V-neck. Thin ankles, in fully-fashioned grey lisle, showed briefly between the hem of her dress and the soft leather tops of her Louis-heeled shoes. Miss Myrtle was still pretty; her face was unwrinkled and her eyes were blue behind small, shiny spectacles. Silver hair, now plaited around her head, fell nearly to her waist when loosened for brushing at night. When she was a girl she had been what her Mother had called a "minx" but any cherished dreams had died on the Somme and only a sepia ghost-image in her gold locket remained of what might have been.

TE—D

49

She took her duster outside, shaking it vigorously into the cool spring air. She looked up towards St. Mark's and down towards the Square, but the pavement was deserted. Only the baker's lad whistled by, scorning to hold the handlebars as he lurched along the middle of the street.

A ginger cat slept in a basketful of ribbon remnants, warmed by pale sunshine that puddled the window. Miss Myrtle paused before she climbed the step into the shop. She tapped at the pane with her fingers and the cat stirred, stretched, then rose to rub his nose deliriously against the glass. He subsided to soft-foot amongst packets of press-studs, fan-spread knitting patterns and several piles of art felt. Then he jumped through the half-curtain that divided the window display from the shop and met his mistress as she unlatched the door and stepped inside.

This was a quiet day in the shop and the sisters had accustomed themselves to a routine that suited them. Miss Patience, on Mondays, did the washing. With best soap flakes she tenderly cared for their Chilprufe under-wear and for the silk blouses that she wore with her dark serge skirts. Younger than Miss Myrtle, she had recently rebelled against the ravages of yet another birthday. A mahogany tint had left her hair a dull scorch-brown and the clown-patches of rouge and smudgy red lipstick had made her sister comment, sarcastically, that it was a blessing that Mamma had not lived to see this day!

Twisted skeins of pure wool were pigeon-holed at the back of the shop, tempting with their exultant splodges of scarlet and yellow, emerald, blue and pink. But Miss Myrtle reached expectantly for the duller colours when Gran seated herself on the bentwood chair and leaned her elbows on the table. It was always grey for Grandad's and Uncle's socks, brown or grey for their pullovers. How they must long, Lucy sometimes thought, for something brighter to cheer their mud-coloured lives.

Gran had taught Lucy to knit. Miss Patience helped by

rummaging for a box of rainbow wool that magically changed colour, with each succeeding row. "All little gels should knit and crochet", she agreed. But Lucy's excitement had waned as the pins got warm and sticky and the stitches tight. A dropped stitch, chased, was liable to split and the work that grew so slowly often finished up disappointingly uneven and definitely grubby.

Bessie bought dishcloth cotton, oatmeal-coloured, to make udder cloths for her cows. "Washes the muck off, luv. We don't want it dropping in the milk!" Miss Myrtle blushed, uncomfortable with a subject that embarrassed her. Corsetry, for the same reason, was discreetly stored, tissue-wrapped, in long flat boxes under the table. A hand-written notice in the window invited prospective customers to "step inside without obligation to view high-class corsetry and lingerie of distinction". Of course, some drapers nowadays fitted their windows with such garments, blatantly displayed for gawping eyes, which horrified the genteel sisters and would have enraged their Mamma.

Mary shunned Market Day whenever possible, for she and the sisters enjoyed her leisurely visit. She valued their advice and they appreciated her skill and, as experts, admired the finished pieces of work that she brought for them to see. Miss Patience brought home-made ginger wine in a glass so exquisite that Mary was a little afraid to be entrusted with it. Each sip went down rich and warm, happily accompanied by some of the cherry cookies that Mary had made for her friends to try. Before she left, Miss Patience had copied the recipe into her own book, afterwards adding a P.S. — "these would benefit from just a little more sugar".

Although the drapery stock was not extensive, its availability was completely reliable. Butter muslin was kept for the curd cheese makers, for jelly bags and for beaded covers to keep flies from milk jugs in summer.

Unbleached sheeting was popular and cheap and, as Auntie said, came up lovely and white after a couple of good boilings! There was a small range of patterned nets (mostly for parlour windows in the town, prying eyes being less troublesome in the country). Miss Myrtle would unroll the bolts, thumping them over and over on the table, knowing when sufficient had been released for measuring by her brass-tipped yardstick. Many a small girl was fascinated when, after a preliminary nick in one side, some materials were torn confidently across with an exciting noise and a tiny flurry of dust. But nets needed cutting with the huge, scrunching pair of shears; customers assisting by holding and smoothing the opposite side.

Pealing bells summoned the sisters gladly to church every Sunday. At Matins and Evensong they sat near the aisle on the second pew, finding in the sermons a source of discussion and inspiration to last throughout the working week. Soon it would be Easter and, in new coats and hats and with the chamois gloves that they wore all summer, they would walk briskly, breakfastless, to the seven o'clock Communion.

From the Hilltop

S am came at last to the top of the steep track and hooked his stick over the fence. Rummaging in the pocket of his jacket he took out a soft brown pouch and, without looking, collected the tobacco and pressed it with a finger into the bowl of his briar pipe. He lighted it, placing the yellow box of matches flat to draw the flame . . . then rested his elbows gratefully on the greened rail and contentedly contemplated the spread of his world.

The homestead lay below him, sheltered in a grassy dimple from the winds that so often wailed sighing across the curve of hills. The roof was golden orange and the kitchen windows glinted in the afternoon sun; fat washing tugged at the line and apple trees frothed beyond the lawn that yesterday he had mown, leaving the striped effect that showed even from the hilltop.

His youngest grandson had run alongside, chuckling just as his father had done when daisies were propelled, pinging, and stinging, against his sunburnt face. The old wooden horse on wheels, faithful in its third generation of paint and with refurbished mane and tail, was pulling a cardboard carton laden with cool and scented mowings and attached by lengths of plastic twine. Afterwards, Sam's daughter-in-law had brought them beer and lemonade and they had all sat together for a while on the white garden seat.

The barn and cart-shed, and the L-shaped cowsheds with blue slate roofs, were the original buildings. They huddled around the house, conveniently close when there were heifers to calve or when the lambing flock was brought in during bitter nights of the youthful year. But recently there were additions of asbestos-capped Dutch barn and covered yard, tall silo towers and a new unit for Jim's Landrace sows.

Behind the barn was the cottage where Shep still lived, enjoying the comparatively easy life of roaming at ease among his memories, reviving old ones with close interest in the new. Sam had never known the farm without Shep . . . when his own father had died he had naturally and thankfully taken on the elderly man, friend of his childhood, along with the farm, the waggoner, the cowman and stock. Shep in his dotage regarded the Suffolk flock as his own and still commented on young gimmers that carried characteristics of a certain breeding line; wisely Sam always sought the old man's advice before drawing the ram lambs for the sales.

Sam's white hair lifted slightly in the breeze; the day hummed with bees, white butterflies fluttered like tossed paper scraps and a scarlet ladybird, in seven-spotted glory, ambled up a twisting blade of grass. The sky sang with lark-cadence, the lovely sound maybe unnoticed by Sam's long-accustomed ears. For now his eyes were busy, sliding over the surrounding slopes as far as the wood, where tall trees stood sombrely dark in the distance, marking the brink of the farm. Barley fields rippled, tawny green lakes surrounded by hawthorn hedges. There were roses behind him on the track, sunwarmed white and porcelain pink, delicate on tousled tangle of thorny hedge. In the autumn Maisie would come up here with the grandchildren, to gather brambles where the thickets would be wealthy with purple fruit and where day-moths and hover-flies now worked among strands of lilac-mauve flowers.

The Clydesdale mares were in the Home Field. Sam could discern Blossom with the white blaze and darker Queenie with her cavorting filly foal. As a younger man he had worked the horses, ploughing when time was daylong and the pace was that of a man's two feet. Then there was rest at each headland and still an acre a day could be turned on good going with a single furrow plough. Eight strong legs, feathers beaded and clotted with damp earth and kindly heads bowing with honest effort . . . the horses preceded the man who followed with booted steps, plough lines wrapped around his hands, screaming gulls and scavenging crows for company and the stirring scent of soil and horse in his nostrils.

Muck-carting or hayraking, drilling and rolling, harrowing and corn-carrying, always there were horses and dogs. Now he could see Jim down there in Bluegate, the red tractor hauling the rotary mower at a swishing pace, swathes falling thickly and the area of standing grass diminishing with every round. What sport he had known when, as a boy, he had gone rabbiting in the hay or when the binder clattered along, leaving plump sheaves to be stooked. He remembered the thistles in his hands at night and the red scratches on bare forearms . . .

From across the village came shouts and laughter as the playground filled with an avalanche of children, out for afternoon break. His own studded boots had once scraped in the paved yard, as had Jim's sturdy shoes and as would those of the newest little ones. Maisie had grown up in the School House. Among the rookery elms he could see the church where she had become his wife. Then he was a young man in khaki, soon to leave his father to till the English land and himself to discover turbulent seas and then the hostile beaches of Normandy.

Jim now lived in the farmhouse. Sam had been persuaded to build a bungalow in Corner Piece near the village. Maisie had earned an easier life after years in the old house with its oil lamps and flagstones and all the work so gladly undertaken, accomplished and shared. Nowadays she had a bright new kitchen with gadgets and serried cupboards, that were well away from the heaviest invasions of straw and chaff, and an extra hour in bed each morning. But still she walked Nell the labrador across to the farm every day, using the dog as an excuse perhaps, for it was hard to be completely separated from the stage whereon most of her life had been set.

Maisie was coming now across the field; Sam could see the bright blue of her dress. She waved and Nell saw him and came lumbering and lolloping up the hill. He bent to stroke the thick black coat, accepted the adulation of brandy-brown eyes, saw the pleasure of that waving tail. Together he and Maisie turned to walk slowly along the track towards Top Field where the Hereford sucklers were grazing. One white face was raised as they approached and Bessie, a matron of the herd, shambled to greet them. Maisie scratched the curly poll, then affectionately slapped the brown-red neck. Bessie's calf, forelegs splayed for take-off, watched from a sensible distance. Nell flopped panting at Sam's feet and the joyous summer day was complete.

Colin Carr

Colin Carr

The River

The auburn hillside, bracken-clad, sloped to where a gentle river meandered, golden as thin treacle, its fingertip shallows chattering over a pebbled bed near an ancient, gazing bridge.

Septimus ambled along the path. His daughter had been peeved with him for accepting another pup after old Prince had been laid, tenderly and reverently, beneath the plum tree; she had embarrassed him, too, by trying to make him, like a naughty child, return the dog to Luke, the waggoner. She was a good lass, really, blessed by a husband and family; her father missed, more than she could possibly have realised, the compensating presence of his dog, the understanding wisdom of brown eyes and soothing comfort of a nuzzling nose.

Young Bob was making a big dog . . . now he bounded ahead, leapt splashing to slake his thirst. Back he came, grinning, boisterous, shaking bright water from a coarse black coat. He was labrador, airedale, collie and perhaps rough terrier, and Carrie despaired whenever she came over to clean. He was muddy, smelly, clumsy . . . and he moulted hairs on the couch where

Dad allowed him to lie like a dirty, friendly rug. But without Bob and his daily walks Septimus might have slumped dozing by the fire in his alms-house kitchen, listening for every moan from his ageing back and every complaint from creaking limbs. Bored into daytime sleep he would have been wakeful in the lonely, interminable nights. Nine years ago he had left the farm and on almost every ensuing day his two feet and supporting thumb-stick had stumped from his garden gate to the ash-tree by the stile. Here he hotched himself to sit, filling failing eyes with familiar sights, shaping memories to colour his dreams. He took a bag of wine gums from his pocket, selected a black one and pushed it into a mouth unimpeded by teeth. Soon he whistled the exploring dog and turned for home. Testing, pleading for a longer walk, Bob briefly resisted, then eventually followed and overtook his master.

Sammy had called for Ron, paper-bagged sandwiches and a bottle of dandelion and burdock stowed in his army surplus gas-mask holder. Mum had bought it from Milletts (and might also have given her boy the moon). A webbing strap crossed Sammy's grey-pullover'd chest, the over-large, heavy and beautiful bag bounced satisfactorily against his side as he walked. He waited for his friend, pulling off his wellies one at a time against a stone by the path, heaving up socks that had already gone thrice to bed. Ron saw Sammy and, immediately, Sammy's khaki bag . . . enviously he unfastened then re-fastened the brass-ended straps, then shrilled for his Mother who came out rubbing wet hands on the wrung floorcloth. She inspected and admired, said nothing, but patted Ron jokingly on the head before going indoors. All down the lane to the river a small hope whispered in the boy's ear . . . "Next week, next week . . . perhaps!" Today an ordinary carrier held ketchup sandwiches, an out-of-season mincepie and an apple; in his hand he clutched his precious new boat. Dad had helped to make it, on these last few companionable evenings in the shed. They had fashioned the hull from a thickish lump of wood, with three skewers from the kitchen drawer for masts. Dad had used the chisel but Ron himself had drilled holes for the masts, then painted the craft (and most of his fingers) with red and white gloss paint. Mum had cut triangular sails from the remnants of a sides-to-middle sheet. Then, with the boat securely held in the vice, Ron had named her with a soft pencil. . . he sharpened it several times and went over and over the letters until *Queen Mary* stood out shiny and black and bold. Dad said Queen Mary wasn't a sailing ship, but her builder, owner, captain and crew cared not even a niggling thought.

Vera and Margaret had settled down into elderly contentment. Neither considered herself old, but nowadays they found themselves surrendering to the needs of broadened, flattened feet, matching and pampering them with broad, flat shoes instead of ignoring their pleas for the sake of pinching smartness. They wore sensible hats because there was sufficient wind to friz Vera's perm and Margaret was suffering from a snuffly cold. For that reason, although she was far too hot, she wore her coat well belted and buttoned; she was also scarved, gloved and camphorated oiled. Both women had weeks ago changed into the whole panoply of winter underwear (the "back end" being such a treacherous time of year). Consequently they were puffed and grateful to rest, leaning against the bridge, to talk a while. Margaret's basket was heavy from the village shop, but Vera was going further up the hill to collect dry sticks for to-morrow's kindling.

Tony had been fretful all night; wailing outbursts and one bright red cheek still defied the attacks of gripe water and teething jelly. Finding her granddaughter distraught, Miriam had tucked the baby into the big deep pram, safe from draughts, and trundled him off down the path.

Spurned leaves twirled from the trees, scrunchy-brown from the sycamores, yellow-blonde from the ash. Michaelmas daisies and pink ice-plants in cottage gardens were thronged by hover-flies and by feasting butterflies with shivering velvet wings. A magpie bounced along a rickety fence . . . Miriam tipped the pram so little Tony could see the smart, wickedly handsome bird. "One for sorrow . . ." she mused, then, jubilantly ". . . two for joy!" as a partner flew, clattering like castanets, to join the first. The baby chuckled, jigging excitedly on his pram-straps. Gran Miriam pushed on. She was singing now, funny little husky snippets from her youth . . . none heard her save a sleepy child, a pathside horse, and a hunting cat that spared merely a half-glance as it crouched quivering under the hedge. She stamped her feet and clapped her hands, concerned for any threatened, grass-scurrying mouse.

Sergeant-Major Hubert's own tiny stream flowed through a miniature bridge in his rockery, hastening to join the river. His cottage, knee-deep in chrysan-themums and late-blooming roses, was pretty enough for a picture postcard. Once an artist in a floppy hat and paint-splattered smock had sat daylong, setting forever on paper the cottage dressed gaily for spring in tulips and aubretia. The picture, brought so unexpectedly by "Postie" one morning, now hung over the fireplace in the living room to greet Hubert as each morning he unlatched the stairs door.

Hubert's shirt-sleeves were neatly rolled; sparse strands of disciplined hair Brylcreem'd across his head were strictly cut to be well clear of ears and nape. A suspi-cion of moustache was so well trimmed as to be barely existent. The professional polishing of an already gleam-ing brass doorknocker, the deep shine on his boots and the knife-crease in chalk-striped, grey trousers were legacies of proud days in the Regular Army. He always lived an ordered, military life . . . still he snapped

instantly to the salute whenever *God Save the King* blared from the ornate silken front of his wireless set. His wife had died before the war . . . their only son had carried the family tradition across perilous waters to Normandy and, much later, home again intact and enhanced. Next week, with his ex-ATS wife and young dark-haired daughter, he was coming to visit. Hubert whistled happily, anticipating some trips in the Morris saloon that Mike had saved so hard to buy.

A narrow field reached towards the riverside. Frank worked the rows of mangolds and swede turnips, pulling them then chopping the tops, throwing the roots into convenient heaps for carting. He hacked a sliver of swede, rubbed it on a mud-tracked sleeve and straightened his back for momentary ease as his teeth crunched noisily into the sweet crispness. Marauding rooks swaggered about the next field where winter wheat had been sown. Disdainfully they plundered and scratched within yards of a one-legged scarecrow that flapped frayed sacking arms, grinned from a straw-stuffed cloth face and pointed a mock gun harmlessly, ridiculously, to the sky.

Ayrshire cows, beautiful creatures with brown and white patched bodies and graceful horns, grazed the rolling meadow that curved beside the river bank, its greenness contrasting with the dry hillside opposite. In midday heat the cattle had stood in the cool water; homewards now at milking-time they wandered, urged by a farm-tousled woman in her print dress and straw hat. Madge's hand rested affectionately on the oldest and slowest cow, her stick never used for striking but only to safeguard each footfall in the hoof-pocked roughness of the trampled ground.

Gran wheeled the pram through the gateway, carefully, delicately, for Tony lay sleeping. A line of nappies flapped in the breeze, Kathy's hair was still damply set in snail-curls after a leisurely shampoo with green soft soap. A short sleep had refreshed her and tea was brewing in the brown, cosy-cuddled pot.

The *Queen Mary* had been launched, splashed with burdock for luck. Ron's Mother had added an item to next Wednesday's shopping list and Vera's firewood was neatly stacked inside the brass fender. Margaret was darning socks and the Sergeant-Major was enjoying a bottle of stout.

A flotilla of dead leaves travelled onward with the river; swallows swooped to kiss the water, frenziedly twittering as their gathering flocks prepared for departure. The grey stone bridge gazed calmly up river and down, watching as one more century slipped inexorably past.

The Farm Sale

L eo from the next farm rattled into the yard in his held-together car, muddy water slurping in twin brown waves as the vehicle lurched through the deeply-puddled gateway. Dad paused, lowering the handles of the wheelbarrow and resting fists on hips. Jimmy, the young foreman, was perched on the pigsty wall, thoughtfully aiming little balls of moss at the sow mountain that lay contentedly grunting below, as nine pink satin piglets jostled, squealing, at their breakfast. The conversation that seeped through Jimmy's ribbed woollen balaclava became more and more interesting . . .

"Old divil laid on two in the night . . . "

"Reckon we shall get some more rain . . . "

"Thought I might have a look over the hill at old Taylor's sale . . .."

"Hang on ten minutes and I'll come with you . . . "

The back door was hurled back against the wall, shaken-off wellingtons landed with rubbery thuds on the back kitchen floor. A small figure with trailing socks came shouting into the kitchen, words jumbling forth to be translated into sense by Mother's accustomed ears.

But Mum fussed so much, making the impatient child wash his face and put on another pullover and an extra pair of socks; then she went through the rigmarole of telling him to be a good boy, to keep with Dad and not touch the car door handles or lose his gloves. Far too slowly she made cocoa for a flask and put two slices of cherry cake into a paper bag. Even then she personally stowed him in the back of Leo's car and stood waving as though they were off to unknown Africa. The throaty whirring became a rackety roar, drowning the rest of Mum's instructions as the old car pulled away, with Dad and Leo in the front and a wildly excited six-year-old riding like a travelling king in the back.

Along the narrow lane they went, where trees met overhead in an archway of interlocking black twigs; ploughed fields were brown and dark on either side, long furrows shining into the distance and lapwings and tattered rooks searching in the cold earth. Sparrows rose in chattering mobs from verges and hedges, fluttering with alarm and settling again when the noisy vehicle had passed, leaving its smelly cloud of fumes and a parallel row of wheel-marks in the beet-muddied surface of the road.

Over the hill the road became broader as it made its way towards the Black Swan Inn and the turnpike. On the left a flapping poster on a gate-post pointed rather vaguely to "THE SALE — THIS DAY". The field was full of people. Surely everybody was there, from Jimmy's village and all the villages around, and perhaps even from the market town. They had come in cars and vans and in farm carts converted to trundle along behind tractors. Some had come on bicycles and others had tied ponies to the fence and left them to nuzzle into nosebags as they stood patiently between trap shafts.

Into the throng went Jimmy, running a little to keep pace with Dad whose big hand securely held his own woollen-gloved one. Hunched, hands in pockets, the assembled crowd moved down the lines of implements,

discussing, appraising. Here was a horse-rake with iron seat held high . . . there a binder and a broken Cambridge roll. Further down the field was a good strong muck-cart, upended so that its shafts seemed to point at the clouded sky. Jimmy poked with his foot at a pile of harness, mentally calling them "oss gears" as Dad would do. The bridle was broadly strapped with thick black leather, coarsely stitched, and the buckles were brass, all polished by use; along the ridges of the saddle were studs and hearts that someone had picked out with silver paint and the padding of the collar still held ginger horsehairs on its grey checked surface.

Jimmy huddled closer among the crowd that shoved and sheltered him; he was swept along like a small pebble in a tide of boots and leggings and muck-encrusted wellingtons, of army surplus greatcoats and farmyard trousers.

"What am I bid, gentlemen?" The auctioneer's boots were polished, his riding mac was stiff and white; he wore a strange hat with a brim at front and back and ear flaps tied beneath his chin. Jimmy watched with awe; peeping between elbows he saw this Being as he passed swiftly by, tapping with his yellow cane as each implement was sold. "Going . . . going . . . gone! And now to the drill, gentlemen. Plenty of work left in it yet. Who'll give me a tenner?"

"Halve it!" came a grunt from somewhere and bids followed rapidly, the auctioneer's voice gabbling on and his eyes shifting from face to face as, bantering and joking, he played friend against friend. Then slap went his cane . . .

TE—E

Wind blew with incredible bitterness along the shivering hedgerows and through the shuddering grass. Jimmy was cold. He stamped his feet and tried to think about warm things . . . like his hot water bottle at night, or the soapy water in the tin bath by the fire and the thick pegged hearth-rug in which afterwards he could twiddle his bare toes. He thought of soup that almost burnt his tongue and of the little whirlpools his breath made when he blew into each steaming spoonful. Tugging at Dad's hand he whispered for permission to go back to the car.

Climbing into the back seat he banged the door, vibrating the yellow mica in the window. He poured cocoa from the flask into its cup, clasping his hands gladly round it and letting the fragrant steam drift damply onto his face. When only a swirl remained he ate a slice of cake, the crumbs falling unheeded down his coat. Pushed into one corner of the seat was an imitation leopard-skin rug and he pulled it up to his chin and made himself small beneath it.

"Get tired of waiting, old son?" enquired Dad as he opened the door to load a big wooden box full of hand tools. But there was no reply.

The foreman was fast asleep.

66

Morning

The house was filled with the clamour of small noises. Rhythmically the clock sent its thudding tick and tock even to the bottom of the back stairs; the budgerigar's feet on his cage floor made a sound like pebbles hurled on a tin roof; the cold water tap shouted "listen!" as it dripped, echoing, into the sink. Hardly had the door latch joined the chorus than the terrier was agog, waiting. The girl, wellingtoned, stroked his head and they walked out together into the veiled dawn of an autumn day.

Behind the farmhouse and beyond the vegetable garden, with its kidney beans and wet red cabbages, was a deep path. This morning it was a cold tunnel where silent mist-soaked maples awaited September sun that would set aflame their orange and amber-crimson leaves. The green-lichened gate opened grudgingly, lifted on the crook of Meg's arm as she persuaded it to let her pass . . . meanwhile the terrier, impatient, squeezed along his accustomed earth-scrabble beneath the fence. Then, in a sparkled and dew-washed world, girl and dog were alone.

Dawn slipped primrose-gowned over the blue-distanced hills, glittering each blade of grass with the touch of her silver slippers. Crystal-beaded spider webs were hammocked between the plantains and gangling white clover. Hawkweeds searched with star-eyes for larks that already dotted the singing sky. Mushrooms were white-domed, cold and hard to the touch, as Meg laid them carefully in her basket . . . softly, gently, so as not to spoil their delicate pink-gilled perfection. The terrier, bouncing, left trails in the misted grass. A leveret leapt away with incredible acceleration . . . that second's worth of stunned surprise delayed the dog and any greyhound aspirations dwindled into a few stiff-legged bounds.

Startled, a pheasant chuckled and rose with whirring wings to blunder across the hedge and flounder into a blue-green sea of kale. From dormitory bushes and from the top of youthful saplings and the browning canopy of great trees came a torrent of bird-song; chirps of sparrow flocks, flute of blackbird and repetitive melody of speck-led thrush. With mustard-dipped head a yellow-hammer flew into a gorse patch, dawdling a while among the golden, vying blooms, to babble about his bit-bit-bit bread and no cheese. Somewhere a great tit uttered his rasping song, but the incessant cooing of wood pigeons soothed again the wounded air.

The criss-cross pasture had yielded a half basket of mushroom harvest before Meg reached the little foldyard at the field's far corner. Young beasts, night-sheltered by a roof of time-darkened straw and brushwood, stood stretching before wandering away to their grazing. Snug in the crannied underside of the old shed top was the blue-tit's nest, now empty, but still a miracle of mysterious love and care expressed in moss and wool and soft feathers.

Meg remembered that magical morning when she had watched, entranced, as seven babies emerged for their initiation into the world. Each blue and saffron scrap had plummeted to the ground, kindly softened as it was with fusty hay and scuffled earth. Somehow the parent birds had located and fed each youngster as it lurched, flower-hopping, on new excited wings.

A late swarm of gnats spun in frenzied dance, whirling and tossing, blurred in their speed. Did they collide or merely circle and avoid as they gyrated here near the stream? The ground was mud-squelched, marked by four dozen hooves multiplied by the tail-winging, thirsty days of summer. Then, plagued by biting flies, the cattle had stood and stamped in idleness. Here shyly, mauvely, had bloomed the lady's-smocks, with pale flowers light as moths on wiry stems. Kingcups had stood knee-deep in the water, pouring a great splurge of gold at the edges of the brown stream; wild mint crushed by hoof or foot was aromatic under the kiss of sun; in this lush environment common daisies had grown tall and large, their faces blushed with comely pink.

Now Meg watched. The youthful stream tumbled and splashed, gurgling and giggling as it fell over tiny water-falls or rippled round reed-stems and over smooth boulders. Small swift fishes darted in deeper forgotten pools, prey for the Kingfisher that speared in blue splendour from shivering silver willows that sentinelled the bank. Soon the stream would flow under the hump-backed bridge in the lane, becoming wider and deeper, darker and more sedate. Meg imagined it brimming broadening as it went, curving in great shining loops across the cattled water meadows. To the fringes of the town it would go, past factories and allotments, blessed with the grace of swans as it swirled at the bottom of backyards and dismal, sleazy streets. She could picture it rolling on relentlessly to meet the swelling tide and rushing untamed to fling itself into the foaming fathoms of surging sea . . .

The girl shook her head and smiled at her dream, here in the cobwebbed grass under the opening eyes of day. The little dog, his coat spiked with drenching dew, questioned her with brown eyes set in his white, tan-patched face. So she turned for home through straw stubble that jabbed at her ankles as though protecting its tiny scarlet pimpernels and baby blue forget-me-nots. Keys hung bunched, weighing down the ash tree branches and a grey squirrel streaked from nowhere, scampering along the ground and then up into a crisping oak already rich with acorn-harvest.

Smoke drifted from the kitchen chimney, clumped Michaelmas-daisies spattered her as she went along the garden path . . . bacon-fragrance met her as it drifted to the door.

The Show

Behind the big grey house swept the parkland, chestnut-studded. Beneath the trees the ground was dry and barren, small deserts in the infinite green that sloped to the very edge of the slow, silver-slithering river. Distantly the clumped woods were blue, black, emerald and yellow; they stood huddled, whispering, guarding nesting pheasants, earth-curled foxes and the badgers that would waddle, pied, to scuffle at night along the moon-shadowed rides.

Greyish marquees had mushroomed overnight. Pennants and bunting were a-flutter; unfurled flags rippled in a wealth of brilliant colours against a white-fluffed July sky. Under a cone of striped awning the men of the Centenary Band matched faces to plum-red uniforms as they laboured strident sound from burnished brass. The "Post Horn Gallop", then an Irish Jig, compelled feet to march or dance in sympathetic rhythm on bruised and pungent sward.

Sam, yesterday, had cut his rye grass. Round and around Daisy and Blossom had hauled the clattering Albion mower. Sam had folded a hessian sack, as semblance of cushion between thin body and jolting, bone-jarring iron seat.To-day the thick swathes lay broad and shining, deserted save for busy swarms of swallows and martins that sped, skimming to feed richly on an easy harvest of disturbed insects. Whilst the once-lush stems wilted and dried, Sam's conscience had allowed him to put on his best suit and go to the Valley Farmers' Grand Agricultural Show.

It had been pleasant to walk with Hilda along summer-dusted lanes, between hedges spattered with roses, pink and white, and verges creaming with Queen Anne's Lace. Hilda wore her vintage grey-flannel costume, somewhat tight over a figure grown definitely though happily buxom. Sam carried the bag with its flask, with milk in a medicine bottle, and sandwiches in a biscuit tin. Sam's mac and her own hung neatly folded over Hilda's arm. Years of Show-going had taught her to distrust even the softest, most promising morning.

Slumbrous, pink, the occupants of a line of pens lay on their sides in deep, clean wheat straw. Disturbed for judging, their dreamy grunts became defiant barks and indignant squeals; guided skilfully, gently, by stockmen's boards and pig-bats they were eventually cajoled to the judging area.

"Cussed critters, pigs", sniffed Shep, derisively. There had usually been a blue-blotched white one, lop-eared, growing monstrous on barley-meal and taties in the pantiled sty at the bottom of his garden — because he enjoyed the near-reesty fat bacon and the Sunday teatime ham. But his mind, his heart, his working life and now his retirement were devoted to sheep. His old eyes watched them and translated what he saw; his numbing ears could still listen for the frantic call of a ewe and was glad when it was tardily answered and ewe and lamb, united, fell silent.

Shep watched as Liz fitted a new white halter over the black face of her young Suffolk ram. The old man had advised on "getting up" the animal for showing and now, after a final ritual passing of his shears over its back, with two courtesy snips that removed nothing (but, Liz affectionately realised, kept him firmly in place as the expert) he stood back to view it from here and from there.

"He'll tek some beating, lass", he told her. "You might even get championship — yon judge be a real Suffolk man". Liz's hopes lifted as a lark to the sky; even the magnificent Longwool with wavy fleece practically reaching the ground, looked less of a threat in consequence.

Terry and Jim, wearing cardboard sun-shades (that also extolled the excellence of someone's fishmeal and feed additives), had already amassed a bundle of shiny leaflets and free catalogues. Chick brooders, paraffin stoves, quack medicines and grass harrows: their sticky hands clasped a treasury of information gleaned from nearly every stand on the showground. Their stomachs were filled with a precarious mixture of strawberry milk-shake, acid drops, Antonio's Pure Dairy Ice-cream and sherbet.

Terry paused briefly, better to manoeuvre a pink gum-bubble that protruded from his mouth, grew, and then prematurely, disappointingly, popped. Jim, meanwhile, made to dive through the door-flap of yet another tent. Dexterously the steward caught his arm, deftly transferring the impetus of his entrance to a thrust-powered exit. Stanley was a lemon-faced little man, dedicated only to the well-being of the rabbits and guinea-pigs that had been his fancy for sixty years gone. Understandably, he did not intend to give wild and whooping young lads the remotest chance of upsetting the charges now quietly nose-twitching in rows of card-bearing cages.

Joseph, ageing clerk from an auctioneer's office, reigned in the Secretary's hut. A beer glass had ringed the top paper of the pile before him, half a ham roll and a jewel-bright tart occupied a cardboard plate. Each November, when the gloomy room in the Corn Exchange hosted yet another Annual General Meeting, Joseph firmly announced his retirement. But (for just one more year) he was perpetually flattered into carrying on. As usual, letters to prospective judges and caterers were scribed in his copperplate hand — entries and draft schedules were peered at through his half-spectacles. His was the organising flair that shaped the Show, his the voice (time-grazed as the day progressed) that ordered and announced. His was the task of calming and comforting when, maybe, a Thelwell pony skirted purposefully round the end of a two foot fence, leaving its rider to clear the obstacle alone.

Intoxicated by the mingling scents of roses, canvas, sweet peas and freshly-watered compost, Bill chatted to a nurseryman. Delphiniums were blue and mauve in steepled opulence; the spurred and graceful aquilegias seemed of some different race from the homely, dark blue "Grannybonnets" that grew beside his cottage path. Sweet peas flaunted, five-flowered, on long straight stems. Mary's windowsill vases held smaller blooms, from parent plants that scrambled unchecked over the trellis near the lawn. The grandchildren, having feasted on warm red strawberries, always came laughing into the house, fists brimming with fragrance (the littlest one was usually content with the clutched head of a dead marigold and a squashy buttercup which Mary floated tenderly, remedially, in a saucer). . . Mary joined the discussion and the nurseryman took out his order book.

Lucy trundled the push-chair; the going was hard on the uneven ground. Her baby brother was well wrapped in his cable-patterned red cardigan that Mother had finished only last night; he chuckled as the windmill that

Lucy had bought for him spun, bright and purring in the breeze. From a stall that was festooned with leather goods, Lucy had chosen a red purse that hung on a strap over her shoulder. It creaked with newness as she unfastened the flap and then snapped shut again the round, shiny press-stud. Father had rummaged in his pocket and found two sixpences which now rattled enchantingly within.

Her Ladyship, in black habit and glossy top hat, trotted by on a tall chestnut whose skin was groomed to veined and gleaming satin. Lucy marvelled at the confidence with which the rider, side-saddle, urged the horse into a warming-up canter across to the woodside.

Liz's Suffolk had earned the coveted red-white-and-blue rosette. Shep sat nearby on a bench, shouting into the cupped ear of a captive listener. Shamelessly he boasted, garrulously explaining the route by which all the good points from his foundation stock had culminated in the girl's fine animal today.

Gran's feet were tired, bulging uncomfortably over shoes that had shrunk a size in the last hour. With cold brisket and limp salad, with urn tea and fondant-covered cakes, she and Grandad were fortified for the walk to the edge of the field where the Morris was parked. A vigorous swing of its starting handle woke it, spluttering, into raucous life. By the time it turned into the farmyard gate, Joseph was shuffling together the paraphernalia of office in his hut. Then he drained his neglected glass, stretched shirt-sleeved arms above his head and allowed himself the luxury of a gaping, cavernous yawn.

Granny and Grandpa

Easter Visit

A pple trees in the orchard paddled in double daffodils. Katy, in the new-born morning, gathered them until one small hand could scarcely encompass the cold bunched stems. Fat buds she picked, and opening flowers that wore ballerina skirts of layered gold and green. From across the yard came the clatter of buckets and boots as Father finished the milking; Joe whistled as he carried hay to the calves.

Mother's zip-topped hold-all stood ready in the back kitchen, together with a heaped basket and her best brown handbag. Smut rubbed his furry black body against a chair, backwards, forwards, round and around. He rose on his back legs, purring loudly as he explored the tantalising scents of pig's fry and dressed chicken, boiled ham and faggots, that came richly from a brown paper carrier to reach his kitten-nose. Mother was deftly wrapping in newspaper, two by two, the big brown eggs that she had collected last evening from the rickyard nests — finally she put the packages gently into a cardboard box. Katy tied her flowers with raffia, scarcely believing that this day had really come at last.

The ferry-bulk came gliding in, less like a vessel than a monstrous wooden shed. It was even a bit, Katy thought, like Noah's ark. She clung rather more tightly to Mother's Harris tweed sleeve, nervous to step aboard and to climb the narrow metal stairway that clanged beneath her feet. But she felt more secure in the saloon with its salt-grimed windows; Mother fetched two cups of tea and some buns with shiny tops and peeping, dotted currants. Suddenly it happened, as she knew it would — the jetty began to move, sliding away up river. Katy laughed at this strange phenomenon, then in a moment the darkly wet, wooden piles were motionless again and the ferry instead was pulling out on its voyage. The water was pewter-grey, each living ripple touched by scintillating light. No crests creamed on wave-tops but a small company of white gulls idly dozed on the deep. Eddies and complicated swirls, patches of smoothly sinister water, showed where currents tugged and lured. A barge passed by and three men waved from its tarpaulined top, heels drumming on the side of their ugly, workaday craft. Just visible was a trawler, far out in the Humber estuary and heading for the open sea. Steadily the ferry approached the opposite pier.

First the ferry and then the train; excitement increased as each small ritual slotted into its own delightful place in the visit to Granny and Grandpa. There was a Nestlé's chocolate bar, thin as thin in its scarlet wrapper, to exchange for a penny in the slot machine. Racing pigeons cooed softly from a pile of baskets, their feet pattering among wood shavings. The glass of the train windows had its own peculiar smell and so had the white whorls of smoke that seeped between the boards of the station bridge — everywhere there was the pervading reek of fish.

Granny waited against the iron front railings, beside the two prunus trees. Her pretty white hair curled softly round her smiling pink face, and her arms were already outstretched to clasp the travellers to her. Katy felt the familiar pressure of the cameo brooch against her ear . . . then Grandpa, tall and thin, came down the path, taking the pipe from his moustached mouth and asking them about the journey. The path was tiled in pink and yellow and the same design continued right into the house and down the hall to the kitchen door; Granny always scrubbed it on her hands and knees, with hot, hand-reddening water and marbled blue soap on a fiercely bristled brush.

Mother was a great talker and she and Granny had three months' news to exchange. The chatter went upstairs and down again, out into the garden and round to Mrs. Next-door. It babbled on all through dinner and above the sounds of washing-up. Grandpa winked at Katy as, later, he put on his hard grey hat and helped Granny on with her coat — "They'd talk the hind leg off a donkey!" he said, and held open the front door.

Little shops lined the narrow street. The milliner's windows were arrayed with special Easter hats, all veiled and feathered or trimmed with bunches of floppy flowers. Scuffled sawdust was deep and clean on the wooden floor of the butcher's shop; Granny waited for her order and Katy made swirly patterns with the toe of one shoe. The sweet shop was filled with foil-wrapped eggs, among which lurked Easter bunnies, and fluffy yellow chicks with orange felt beaks and scraggly wire legs. One Easter, Granny had bought Katy a stuffed baby duckling. She had cuddled it in her warm hand, looked sorrowfully at its dulled, staring eyes and tenderly touched the dried leathery webs of its feet. She had taken it home and placed it in a corner of the duck-pen, thinking that miraculously it might find again its life. But the white duck and her own babies had trampled it in the mud as they rushed, waddling, to the pond — Katy had wrapped her duckling in a piece of blue tissue paper and put it with the dolls in her toy box. To-day she chose instead a miniature chest of drawers filled with speckled sugar eggs.

Scone-scent wafted from the kitchen as the mantel-clock sang the teatime hour in its familiar, sonorous voice. Katy ran to the window to watch the plodding horse as it pulled an almost empty coal-dray back to its yard. "Coo-al! Coo-al! Half a bag or a whole 'un!", shouted the grimed and leather-jerkined man who sat behind the horse, anxious to sell out and go home for his own tea.

The evening was cooler and a March lion-wind had risen to flurry the water and blow wave-tops into tossing white crests. The moody tide was wild and frightening, suffering humans to cross yet guaranteeing safe passage to none. "Good job if they could put a bridge across this lot!" Katy stared at the fat man who was leaning to talk to her Mother. She thought of the stone bridge over the beck at home; she thought of the shore so far across this heaving water. Why — you might as well talk of putting a man on the moon!

Great
Grandma

Great–Grandma sat upright, disciplined by a stern yellow-varnished chair. She was afternoon-aproned in starched white over her long black dress with its glinting bands of jet beads; a narrow velvet ribbon encircled her neck. Grey hair, piled in a bun, left clear her gentle, wrinkled face . . . a face frequently crinkled by smiles, as love willed the mazed lines of long life and hardships to yield to the expression of her present contentment.

A fat Bible lay opened on her lap, its centre pages recording the early sadness of her life. For grief had guided the fine steel nib along a scratchy path that was now faded to a shade scarcely deeper than the yellow of the thick, musty paper. Three children had survived, George, Florence and Ellen.

Florence's earliest memory was of being taken by her father to kiss the latest new baby in its little coffin while her mother lay fevered upstairs.

Then the lists of births and deaths ended in a different hand as Great-Grandma herself had added the death at twenty-nine of Ernest her husband (who had "gone into an early decline from the consumption").

But Great-Grandma was not unhappy that afternoon. She was in the midst of the *Book of Psalms* and sometimes sang a few throaty verses, then smiled across at the huge squashy armchair filled with a purring jumble of curled and cushioned cats. They rumbled in fire-warmed slumber, spreading a paw or turning a head; there was Amber, whom Great-Grandma had christened Aubrey; Cupid who had become Cooper; and Pretty and Plainy the long-haired tabby sisters.

Soon the old lady's grand-daughter came into the room . . . "Grandma!", she cried affectionately, "why not let those cats sit on the mat — you'll be weary on that hard chair . . ." Then she bustled about at the hearth. Inside the burnished rails of the brass fender was a warm, soft-brushed territory ruled by two Monarchs of the Glen that ever stared out from their background of dark green tiles. She tidied Great-Grandma's pile of "flashy bits", collected that morning from the dry places under the Home Field hedge, and took the copper kettle from its trivet to set it singing on the glowing fire.

Great-Grandma, bonneted in black straw with bunched violets, enjoyed a walk in fine weather. Across the fields she would wander, or perhaps over the common, stopping for a word with Joey the roadman as he cleared the runnels that drained the surface water. Usually a conspiratorial child would run along at her side, for across the long span of years she had somehow remembered how it felt to be very young and seemed anxious to hand down the important bits of knowledge.

She would perhaps sit for a while on a fallen elm trunk and make a rabbit from wound and twisted stems of timothy-grass (but Great-Grandma called it foxtails). She understood that nothing was more exhilarating than to roll down a slope of thickly daisied grass . . . Gran and Mother saw only the green stains and pretended to be cross! Confidently she joined in the search for fairies in the patch of tall willow-herb . . . well, who could be absolutely certain that those flutterings were really made by small white moths? Wouldn't a dainty fairy, exquisitely dressed in pale green, and with gauzy wings neatly folded, look exactly like the lace-wing resting in a niche on the gate-post?

She knew, too, that there were four-leaved clovers in Bluegate . . . sometimes she used a bit of spit and an odd leaf to keep bright her reputation and she and Kathy laughed together when the trick was discovered! There were many secrets to be learned in those wonderful days and years; scarlet pimpernels closed their flowers before the rain; a morning sky that blazed with orange beauty was a shepherd's warning, but when at evening the same sky was daubed with every nasturtium hue, then the shepherd could rely on to-morrow's fine weather.

Mare's-tails grew under the milk-churn stand, each stem to be disjointed, with the giggled accompaniment of "He loves me! He loves me not!". Indoors plum or prune stones told of marriage with "Tinker, tailor, soldier, sailor . . ." (Gran or Mother quickly spooned another fruit or two into the bowl of any child who miserably pushed the last stone into place with its daunting promise of "beggarman, thief").

Near some cottages at the end of the village was an open ditch. At the approach Great-Grandma would take out a handkerchief that smelled of lavender water and give it to Kathy with instructions to hold it firmly over her nose and mouth. Practically stifled by the sweet smell, scarely daring to draw breath, she was propelled past the hazard . . . for everyone knew that bad smells could cause diptheria.

Nearly home again, the girl would huddle closely to the comforting skirt, clutch tightly the knobbly hand . . . for here at a cottage gate stood Gordon, a boy that so strangely dwelt in the body of a grown man. Gordon beamed, for Great-Grandma would always pause to talk to him, patiently waiting as he manipulated his words, delightedly accepting the rose or dandelion or sprig of privet with which he showed his friendliness. But when Kathy could only look with fascinated horror at the large hands and smiling, dribbled mouth, she would skip away with infinite relief at the parting. Poor Gordon was quite harmless, they told her, and she must always be kind to him and pray for him. So she prayed very hard, hands clasped clammily together under the bedclothes as the nightlight spluttered and danced, making terrible, lurching shadows on the sloping ceiling beside the wardrobe. One day Gordon was no longer waiting at the gate and Great-Grandma assured her that God had taken him into Heaven to make him well. Kathy felt a bit guilty, in case she had prayed too often for Gordon to go away.

When the harvest of cress grown on milk sile pads dampened in saucers came to its amazingly speedy harvest, Mother spread it in egg sandwiches for her Sewing Party teas. These were occasions, too, when lace-edged guest towels hung from the mahogany towel rail in the big bleak bathroom, and tiny tablets of scented pink soap appeared from the top drawer of the spare room chest. Though evenings were dimly lamp-lit and Great-Grandma's old eyes were helped only by spectacles with golden frames hooked firmly around her ears, she still crocheted yards of lovely lace. Pillowcases, sheets, guest towels and damask tablecloths were luxuriously finished with the frosty white edging; the fabric to which it was married with minute stitches was further enhanced by drawn-thread work. Spider web mats sat on dressing tables and under jardinières that held aspidistras and ferns, and the hideous great cactus that sometimes produced an ephemeral scarlet flower of alien beauty. Bone and ivory crochet hooks were carefully stowed in a carved wooden cylinder whose top pulled off with a screech that made Kathy wince and press knuckles to her teeth.

Turning the leaves of a photograph album crammed with snaps, I find one of Harriet Tailby, my Great-Grandma, seated by her front door, a bunch of pink tulips (I *know* they were pink) laid upon her knee. It was her 90th birthday, and beside her stood a little girl with shining, smooth-combed hair, a school tunic and three-quarter length socks.

Was it forty years ago . . . or only yesterday?   □

The Family

I saac shivered on that cold spring morning in 1890, resting his forearms on the low wall that separated the back path of the house from the farmyard.

This had been his home since he had started work as an orphan lad, sleeping in the dusty hayloft but well fed and adequately, if strictly, cared for. Work had brimmed his days, from hoof-clattering early mornings to frosty lamb-pens or lamplit byre at night. He heaved and carted steaming loads of muck, ploughed, harrowed and made hay. He scythed and hoed, broadcast wheat and barley and clover seed. The wind blew the songs from his mouth, a sack over his shoulders was his only concession to rain.

When Missus died, Isaac moved into the house, into the small raftered room beneath the eaves — mice no longer ran over him as he slept, but scampered with scuffling feet night-long in the thatch. In Gaffer's rambling senility, Isaac became his comfort and his son.

Now the farm was all his own, the buildings, garden and orchard, the Pingle, Low Hovels, Bluegate, Home Field and a five-acre parcel of land beyond the brook. There were four milking cows, too. Trotty's ribs, admittedly, were countable beneath her roan hide, her long horns were ridged by years — sometimes she stretched out her head and coughed. But she was a quiet old beast and Gaffer's favourite and would fill the bucket, come

June when she calved. The other three were younger. Given luck and regular dosing with special drench they might avoid the wasting scourge that frequently raged through a herd. There were heifer calves, well-grown, and there would be more. If foot-and-mouth disease threatened, Isaac would protect his stock with eye-smarting reek of onions strewn about the sheds; Old Gaffer's liniments and potions would cure lameness and fevers and bloat.

Ida had been kitchen maid at the Hall when she and Isaac first met. They walked to her parents' cottage in the next village on Sunday afternoons and once, on a visit to the Michaelmas Fair, Isaac had won for her a sparkly glass vase on the Hoop-la. It had then nestled, carefully wrapped, in Ida's bottom drawer (together with the hand-stitched sheets and pillowslips and embroidered chairbacks that she worked in the kitchen, when dinner was cleared and the range still warm). She had been cook for five years and was almost twenty-nine, with brown wavy hair and plump, dutch-doll cheeks, when she married. A silver tea service, engraved with her name and the date, was her reward for faithful service. It stood beside the vase and a pair of china dogs on her new dresser.

Frances was their first child, born in the best bedroom, whose window overlooked the garden and the wood. Owls hooted — and the baby's thin mewling cries replied as the sun trailed orange robes across the dawn. Frances was a fretful baby, but scarcely was she a year old when Fred arrived, so good by comparison that Ida hardly knew she had him. Two years later Edith was born, then Henry.

Isaac collected cow-heel bones for "snobs" for his children — iron hoops were fashioned at the smithy for them to trundle with dreadful clamour along the rutted lanes. The girls had rag dolls and one waxen-faced beauty who was partially melted when a curled cat spent a sleepy afternoon in the cardboard-box cradle. Fred and Henry played with celluloid cows, lions and a tiger and a clockwork clown who danced on the table, waving a rubber ball on a stick.

Then the delighted girls had no need of toys. When Henry was eight their mother had another child. Wilfred's sisters wheeled him out in the wickerwork perambulator that was no longer required at the Hall. They combed his fair hair, wonderingly curling the shining strands around their fingers. They sang to him and crooned as they rocked him to sleep. They laughed with him when cherry petals drifted like snow as they all sat on the grass. But there was no strength in his thin legs, his eyes were huge and in a wan, transparent face. Before he was two, his cocoon of love could hold him no longer. Father said he was in a happier land — but his family's world was dark and cold.

Frances grew to be a bundle of a girl looking, her mother said, "like a sack of potatoes tied up ugly". Her hair always strayed from its pins and her hands were red-chapped from harsh soap and harsh work — almost as rough as the scrubbing brush with which she rasped the red brick floors in dairy and scullery and vast farm kitchen.

Edith was dainty, her frizzy dark hair remained high-piled and secure. She was perhaps a little vain; often, in the candlelight, she twirled before her specked bedroom mirror, pleased by the swirl of silk dress around her slim figure. "Our Edie", said her father, whose constant delight she was, "is a cut above the rest . . ."

Fred tilled the land and did the milk round. He harvested fallen apples for sale and made thumb-sticks and spill holders from glossy cherry wood. He was gangling-tall, nearly bald at forty, slow-plodding in his leather gaiters and heavy boots. His untrimmed moustache was snuff-stained; tremendous sneezes shook his whole being as a result of his indulgence.

Edith sometimes stayed with her cousin in town. There she met a studious young clerk who wore small glasses, and dark suits with watch-chained waistcoats. He gave her an engagement ring of clustered pearls, like a tiny flower. Isaac was proud of his daughter — Ida was uneasy, unsure, confiding to Frances her fear that pearls always meant tears. Once engaged, Edith seemed reluctant to marry — "Wait until after harvest", she pleaded, or, "Not until Christmas is over . . ." Months later, anxiously it was "When mother is better . . ."

But Ida was never again to rise from the big brass bed. She lay, small against the plumped pillows, the household reins still guided by her frail hands. Frances trotted to obey her every command, seeking permission for the opening of a jar of fruit or the setting down of eggs in waterglass. When one day she broke the blue milk jug she buried the pieces in the garden, afraid of being scolded like a careless child. Henry, Ida's adored youngest, sat by his mother's bed, brought his new ferret to show her, and even amused her with his privileged teasing.

Edith's Walter finally rebelled. He met and married a girl in town and Edith sued for breach of promise. Her disappointed father became a saddened, bent old man.

He was killed by a strike from a young cart stallion that he had bred.

On a wild day of storm, a more terrible storm exploded in Edith's brain. She flung wide her bedroom window and, screaming, tossed her possessions into the yard. Handkerchiefs and a stocking caught in the lilac tree — a white shoe splashed among the amazed ducks, momentarily floating before disappearing below the green surface. Coins, beads and a work-box were hurled to the cobbles — Edith leapt after them and survived the fall for only a few minutes.

Ida, fortunately, had retreated into a dream world; kindly twilight veiled the tragedy from her consciousness. Frances tenderly cared for her, passing for Edith in the old woman's half-sight and the dim room. Ida, weary, slept and died. Muddled by grief, Henry walked the fields and struggled through the wood — he sat on a fallen tree and moaned till he was exhausted. The gamekeeper found him, with his face bramble-clawed. Gently he helped him home. From that day Henry spoke no more than incoherent mumblings. Working and only briefly sleeping he stumbled through two more years before he was carried to join the mother that still he mourned.

Fred and Frances now sat, one each side of the kitchen, at nights. Fred, in the upright Windsor chair, reread a Western that Ida had once bought at a jumble sale. Frances sang hymns, tunelessly, querulously. A bottle of port stood beside her on the floor; greedily, between verses, she gulped the wine from a cup. She rocked and rocked as the fire burned to grey ash.

Seven ivied stones stand in a row. The grass is untended about the graves and the yew hedge moves slightly in the wind.

Callers

His boots were two great splodges, flat, string-laced. A greasy hat slouched over eyes that, together with a pock-marked nose, were scarcely visible amongst scorchy-grey vegetation of hair and beard. His figure was shrouded by a greening frock-coat, for which some scarecrow possibly now shivered. Over his shoulder hung a bulky sack, making him look, Rosie thought, like a slow-slithering snail, its world on its back.

Frantic dogs loudly warned of the stranger. Jed, the collie, sped in ever-decreasing circles, plumed tail waving as he pranced and barked. Chip stood firmly, threateningly, on short splayed legs, back cresting from neck to rump. A terrier-snarl, out-menacing Jed's noisier excitement, crescendo'd from under the wrinkled lip that bared her armoury of small white teeth. The tramp waited uncertainly near the garden gate, waving defensively with his stick. Father, from the meal-house door, shouted in the fierce voice which Jed instantly (and Chip reluctantly) obeyed.

Rosie, surprised, watched an unexpected smile crumpling the man's grimed face — but she clung closely against Mother, fearful that he might perhaps come near and pat her head. She was glad of Father's whistling presence across the yard.

"Would there be a sup, Missis? Or perhaps Boss has a job needs doing? Nothing heavy, mind, for I've a terrible wicked back . . ."

He sat under the ash tree, on the dying autumn grass. With both hands he gripped the pint basin into which Mother had poured his tea . . . with slaking, mannerless slurps he gulped the hot brown brew. From the kitchen window, the cotton-smell of the curtains reassuring her and Chip alert beside her, Rosie watched. Setting down his half-emptied basin, the tramp broke the crusty top of cottage loaf that Mother had given him, dunking each piece before greedily, urgently, pushing it into his hungering mouth. There was a hunk of red cheese, too, which he hacked with a stub of broken knife and posted, rind and all, after the bread. Then, replete, he settled down on the ground, put his hat over his face and folded his hands across his stomach. With his head resting on the sack, feet lolling sideways, and with snoring breaths drawn thunderously into a sagging mouth, he slept.

★   ★   ★

Edie came on Tuesday afternoons and every other Friday. Great Aunt (who occasionally came to stay and was a bit posh in her ways) called her "The Woman". It was odd, Rosie pondered, that Great Aunt could walk into a room and never notice Edie at all, even though Edie was fat and wore bright colours and nearly always sang as she worked; if they met in the passage or on the stairs she merely gave what Father called her "gracious nod" but never spoke. When Aunt was staying, poor Edie had her tea and biscuits alone in the back kitchen. But on ordinary days, when the atmosphere was warm and comfy as a woollen vest, she sat with her elbows on the in-kitchen table, telling Mother (sometimes in tantalising whispers behind her hand) all the gossip from the village. Rosie skipped about companionably with Edie who often hugged her squashy-tight with a free arm, laughingly asking if she *ever* stopped chattering?

Together, Mother and Rosie and Edie cleaned silver and brass. They told the child that nothing was better than "Elbow Grease" for furniture and Rosie, mystified, polished and polished with the fluffy yellow duster until, magically, her own face smiled, blurry, from the whorled depths of the walnut dining table.

Edie had a boy and a girl. Terence had recently gone to work in the hardware shop in town . . . he wore a khaki-brown warehouse-coat that, in its unshrunken newness, swamped his gangling fourteen-year-old figure. He was clever and grown-up and handsome, and Rosie loved him. Pam was ten and, in the school holidays, came to play with Rosie while their mothers worked. In the secret space between the tall snowberry hedge and the old and hugely overgrown laurel bush they kept their own house.

Leaves and acorn cups, pieces of bark and fragments of blue slate set their table. Teddy and Pink Rabbit, Arabella and Golly and Big Betty with the sleeping eyes and golden ringlets were their children. Wet days sent them instead to the attic. In trailing pieces of tablecloth, hobbling in Minnie-Mouse shoes or dressed in Grandmother's feather boa and her lushly-trimmed hats they were princesses, royally oblivious of the weather that wept against the peep-windows of their palace.

★   ★   ★

The "Thursday Man" had a tall van that rattled and swayed along the rutted track. Lamp oil was carried underneath the vehicle in a tank; tins and measures swung, jangling, near the brass tap. During the week

Mother accumulated her copy-pencill'd list. "Don't let me forget to put that down for the Thursday Man . . ." she would say as she ran out of Robin Starch, or of Zebra for the range.

"Hullo, Thursday!" Rosie greeted as she ran out with the list. "Hullo, lassie . . ." he answered, "and how's the world using you, then?" Mother came out and they climbed a wooden step to go right inside the van, which was fitted with racks and shelves and smelt of soap and disinfectant, matches and Flit and string — with waves of paraffin strongest of all. There were slabs of carbolic and tins of Mansion Polish; there was methylated spirit that Thursday poured carefully, blue and beautiful, into Mother's own bottle. He had saucepans and egg-whisks, enamel bowls and the little wire baskets in which Mother kept ends of soap to make lather for washing-up. There were blue-bags which, strangely, made whites even whiter . . . and also soothed insect stings. Among the lamp chimneys and wicks were hurricane lamps to carry round the yard . . . and candle lanterns for which Rosie yearned in vain because she was too young.

★　　　★　　　★

Father always went into the house when the Corn Merchant arrived, on the first Monday in every month. Thomas bowled up in a varnished trap, pulled at smart pace by Dandy, the skewbald pony.

Rosie sat on the garden wall, feeding Dandy with sugar lumps. Sometimes, on hot days, Mother brought a slopping-full bucket of water. Father, meanwhile, ordered linseed and cotton cake, maybe seed corn or some yellow flakes of Kositos. Jed's big square biscuits came from Thomas and smaller, broken ones for Chip, and he could recommend spices and minerals and cattle licks. Father and Thomas would have a drop of whiskey and then father would take out his cheque book. Some-times, when bristled stacks had been threshed and the sacks of corn hauled to the mill, Thomas would bring Father a cheque . . . then Mother and Rosie had to go to town to the dark and gloomy bank, where caged cashiers sat sternly on high stools, sadly doing sums with scratchy pens . . . and nobody spoke, save in whispers.

★   ★   ★

Parson, black-cassock'd, walked the field path from the back lane and Rosie gambolled to meet him. He stood still as he saw the child, holding wide his arms and smiling his rosy-cheeked Father Christmas smile under breeze-blown white hair. He swung Rosie high in the air, then set her down gently on the grass . . . holding hands they continued the journey together. They laughed at a crow that strutted and pecked, startled a grey squirrel that fled with streaming tail and leapt to high safety of hedgerow sycamore . . . 'midst a scattering of browning leaves.

Rosie stooped for a dandelion clock, puffing one . . . two . . . three . . . teatime! as they reached the door.

The Tree House

The sycamore canopy was coarse lace, its pattern constantly changing as leaves slid across one another in the breeze that whispered softly from the birch coppice. When the dazzling sun-blob hid behind green-clustered branches, everything was sombre, like the dairy . . . or even like Mrs. Squire's drawing-room where once the subdued and fidgety children had been taken to tea (an occasion that had threatened throughout the whole fortnight, after Stevie and Philippa had rescued Squire's mislaid glove from the school path). But when Rosie moved her head very slightly the brightness came dancing through in yellows and palest lacewing-green to dapple the bare ground below.

This was the friendliest tree in the garden; its smooth branches grew conveniently to support the stout cabin that had been fashioned and fixed soon after the summer-house had been built. The summerhouse was a place for Gran with her tapestry, for sleepy Great-Uncle, and for Mother when she podded peas. Stevie, nudged and shushed into silence, used to gaze in amazement as Great-Uncle's hands twitched across a watch-chained waist-coat; eyelids drooped and mouth sagged, lips vibrating to the escaping breath that had been drawn in as a snore. Fancy wasting, thus, even half an hour of a summer after-noon! Rosie and Philippa regarded their Uncle, too, with pity. For he was dressed, winter and summer, in a dark suit, a stiff wing collar and knitted black silk tie. His feet were inescapably laced into shiny black boots of appal-ling stiffness, scarcely cushioned by the grey socks that Gran knitted, round and around on thin steel pins that clicked as they flew.

Great-Uncle was a widower, which was an important but rather sad kind of person to be, so the children had to be extra kind to him; willingly they must run tiresome errands without hopeful thought of the silver threepenny bit with which he might reward them. Nevertheless, the tiny, pretty coin was eagerly accepted and comfortingly clutched while they half-listened to gloomy advice about saving and thrift and rainy days. Poor Great-Uncle! He disliked naughty, happy, nuisance things (like Tom Kit-ten) but enjoyed bread-and-butter and semolina pud-ding. His gold pince-nez reddened the bridge of his nose and left livid marks whenever he removed them and briefly put aside one of the dark brown books whose tis-sue-thin pages were crowded with tiny print collected into long, dreary words.

It was Mother's idea that the children should escape to the trees. She and Father had gazed up into the oak, shak-en the apple boughs, then finally chosen the sycamore. Reuben had cycled round and chewed on his pipe as he mused and measured, then sawed and hammered and smiled. Mother and Gran watched approvingly, happily anticipating the time when the children's activities need no longer mould themselves round the craggy core of Great-Uncle's eccentricity.

There were grey willow catkins, like tiny silky rabbits, in Philippa's treasure-box; her sovereigns were dropped flowerets from St. John's Wort that flowered August-long in the border beside the old wall. Betty, the china doll, slept close by in her cushion-nest and Dear Teddy sat on an upended box, staring through the window with his one amber eye. A pair of toy binoculars hung on a hook and Stevie reached them down and leaned his elbows on the sill to watch the sparrows that hawked for food among the meadow grasses. Starlings, now purple, then green, chortled on the house roof . . . practical jokers they were with their squeaky impersonations of all birdland.

A cock chaffinch flew to perch in the apple tree and a great tit creaked and grated monotonously, somewhere out of sight. Stevie discerned the post van, red-beetling across the landscape; he tried to track peevishly twittering swallows that swooped and soared to mob Mitten Cat as she walked high-tailed, along the fence. Mother's tame blackbird, shabby-plumaged by service to his nestlings, cleaned his bill on a rockery stone and flew down to the back step.

Gran came singing across the garden, placing her laced brogues carefully to avoid the host of infant sycamores that had sprouted among the rough grass. Solemnly she took the Swiss cowbell from a cranny near the bottom of the tree trunk; three dull, flat notes announced her arrival. Stevie, lying on his stomach, let down a weighted string and Gran, saying nothing, would attach a folded note or even a parcel. Clapping her hands twice she signalled for her offering to be drawn upwards into an alien, enchanted world. Gran's messages were always special and the children gathered round to read the clear round writing.

"I am going down to the village in half an hour and shall buy sugar mice and three bars of Nestlé's chocolate" — or, "The Light Sussex hen that laid away, has hatched a nestful of chicks".

Her parcels were even better, perhaps three warm rock buns or a bottle of ginger pop. Stevie would always remember her best-of-all offering, an old alarm-clock that went perfectly as long as it lay flat on its back. Philippa was pleased when Gran's silver fox fur came up on the end of the string, with a note that said "Please can I spend the afternoon with you?"

This was Philippa's special friend. Snuggled against Gran in the box pew on Sundays she would stroke the white-flecked fur, feel the little dry nose and beady eyes; her inspection of claws and satin lining, and the fastening and unfastening of chain and bobble could speed the dreariest of sermons to its close. Sometimes she dozed, her nose buried in the familiar fragrance of camphor and Devon Violet. But up in the tree house foxy came hilariously alive, dancing on short legs, wagging a white-tipped tail and even tangling with Tom Kitten on the dusty floor.

Mother, labelling the last jar of raspberry jam, had been pestered into finding a pensionable tablecloth. Then she had halved it and quickly pressed its hems in place. Now Rosie passed the material through the clackety little sewing machine, tediously turning the handle to produce a gappy lockstitch that was so much more fun than the neat rows of grubby stitches produced under the critical eyes of Miss at school. Stevie opened his tool box; two nails and a piece of tape later, a pair of yellow-checked curtains hung at the window.

A lost white butterfly fluttered through the doorway, settling with quivering wings on a gaudy flower that brilliantly bloomed in a lifeless froth of crumpled scarlet paper. □

Just Another Day

G inger trundled the station truck noisily along on its iron wheels and whistled round to the back door where Mother was busy filling buckets from the soft water-butt.

"Them day-olds came on the earlier train, Missis", he explained, "so I thought I'd best be nipping them round . . . " Mother fetched sixpence from her bag and Ginger touched his porter's cap, stowed the coin in his waistcoat pocket and returned through the wicket gate, along the platform, past Rory's signal box and into the goods yard. Palming his watch he checked it against the placid white face on the waiting-room wall. In precisely nineteen minutes a clamouring bell would warn that the eleven-eighteen had left the next station almost eight miles away and would soon steam importantly into sight, lord of the single track as it pulled two carriages and the guard's van to a squealing halt. Mr. Green, the Station Master, greeted the arrival with due dignity, helping young Peggy to alight and talking in an official way to Bert, the Guard. Ginger, after the train had departed, fussed and finicked with obsessive zeal; Mr. Green personally believed that his porter would prefer a station at which no train ever called . . . then he could sweep and polish, garden and paint without fear of his work being smeared and smutted at the whim of the LNER timetable.

Three cardboard boxes spoke with urgent chirpings as Mother carried them across to the small hut. Tessie bounced beside her on three-year-old legs that, hastily wellied, scarcely paced her exitement. Paraffin-fumed warmth enveloped them as Mother shut the door . . . the wooden floor was clean and dry, fresh from its scraping and hot-soda scrubbing, dried by the Valor heater that now cast misshapen blobs of light upon the swept roof and sides. Tessie, breath held in expectant silence, watched enthralled as Mother opened the first box. Twenty-five primrose-yellow chicks with worm-pink bills and legs called petulantly as they clustered on sawdust, uncertain, afraid. Mother gently lifted one, cupping it between caring hands so that the child could stroke with one finger its soft-downed head. Carefully, so tenderly, the chicks were transferred to the brooder where Putnam lamps warmed the floor; above was the lid with a soft felt cushion suspended to pamper them during their first few weeks, giving comfort, simulating the under feathers of a broody hen.

Meantime, in the hayloft over the calf-pen, a grey banty sat closely, secretly, on her chosen nest, covering her clutch of precious, perfect eggs.

"That banty's laid away again", Joey the farm lad complained as he plodded, laden, into the byre. Often he noticed her as she scratched, fluffed and chuntering, in the dusty flotsam of the passage; he turned his head or reached for the cake ladle and she had gone. Unreasonably he felt annoyed, outwitted by a stupid bird when he reckoned to be so clever! Soon the long vigil would be over, the hatching accomplished. Tiny fluff-balls would tumble from their plateau to land lightly, miraculously unharmed, until eventually the family was mustered. Untamed, they were heirs to a glorious farm-wide freedom, yet pitifully vulnerable to risks too huge for the disproportionate courage of their diminutive parent. Once the rickyard had been overrun with neat bantam hens and with fiercely handsome cockerels that crowed with distorting energy from gate-post or muck-hill, that attacked with beak and spur and that, at dark, roosted high in the raftered barn. Gradually most of them disappeared or died. Fox-reek and feather-trail told of dawn raids and carnage; the old half-wild tom-cat sometimes slept, sated (but by no means blameless), close to the nettle-run. But there was always a straggle of tough survivors that throughout spring and summer struggled to perpetuate, picturesque, glossy-feathered, proud in their independence.

The chicks in the brooder, contentedly crooning, fed and watered and warm, were settling by comparison into utmost luxury.

An ancient hedge, untrimmed, was wealthy with budding maples, bread-and-cheese hawthorns and lambtail catkins. Heather skipped, then hopped, then she turned and walked warily backwards. Learning the new game of "Follow My Leader" was Monica, with her curly fair hair, pleated skirt and robin-red jumper. Heather was in charge of her self-willed younger sister, who had promised to behave but was finding it difficult. But interest in the game had restrained her from the cliff of rebellion and now she giggled happily as she strove totteringly onwards, backwards, then rolled in a heap with her feet in the air. The fence abruptly stopped the game and they squeezed through into the spinney. Grass, in shade, was thick and cool . . . probing fingers soon found the prize that Heather had known would be there. Violet leaves cuddled tiny dark flowers, sweet to the snub noses of the crouching children as they gathered them into finger-posies. Heather chided her silly little sister for plucking such short stalks, but quickly found a root of whitish flowers to show her when Monica's face began to crumple . . . she, in turn, had promised not to make her sister cry. Reconciled they sat lovingly together on a log, binding the bunches with strands of sheeps' wool, oily, grey, that was caught by the wire.

To-morrow, in cups from the dolls' tea service, the flowers would decorate the Mothering Sunday tray alongside a boiled egg dressed in its felt cosy, crustless bread-and-butter soldiers and the special occasion china breakfast cup filled with pale milky tea. Maybe a few tea leaves might float to the top, for Heather was not yet quite certain when the kettle was boiling. But Mother never seemed to mind and would fish out the longest on the tip of her spoon, transfer it to the back of her hand and foretell the visit of a "stranger". Unexpected strangers at the farmhouse were as unlikely as red rabbits at the sand-warren, but the familiar ritual effectively chased away childish disappointment as Mother, without the slightest grimace, drank the cooling brew.

Duchess's great hoof was cradled on Smithy's leather-apron'd lap; yellow smoke puthered as a hot shoe was held in place for fitting. Monty, belted, paunchy, leaned cross-legged against the rough wall . . . his arms were folded as he droned on about the land, the village, the weather (which was always wrong) and everyone else's business. The slumbering furnace reddened into life at Smithy's bidding and sparks flew from pounded metal. Old Leonard paused as he passed, another loose end that habitually gathered at the blacksmith's joining the daily parliament that was vociferous in its powerlessness. Smithy himself, whip-sinewed, continued with his work, grunts and single words sometimes dropping into the conversation, his own thoughts mostly remaining unspoken in his mind. Hoof slivers littered the floor amid an amazing collection wherein each component appeared, nevertheless, to have been dropped in its specific place; Smithy merely reached out a blindly confident hand to retrieve hammer, pincers or fragment of iron as each was required. Now, with Duchess shod, he walked briefly outside, wiped a streaked brow on the back of a grimier hand and enjoyed the flutter of breeze on his face.

Bernie had climbed the old lilac tree and now sat on the garden wall, kicking his heels and picking off pieces of moss to throw thoughtlessly to the ground. His curious gaze was drawn to where, across the churchyard, the gravedigger was working, almost obscured by mourning yews that stood sombrely by the path. Auntie woke from her snooze and missed him; her urgent voice summoned him anxiously, harsh with guilt. Running out she pulled the surprised child so quickly from the wall that accidentally she grazed his leg. She carried him swiftly inside, her hand shielding young eyes from the harrowing scene, kisses pressing his cheek. Behind the slammed door she solicitously, apologetically, bathed his knee, wrapping it with a comforting bandage of clean strip-torn cotton. With lemonade and a picture book she hoped to rinse from Bernie's sight his encounter with one of death's grim panoplies, thus discouraging questions that she felt unable to answer.

The dairy was cold from stone and slate, from flagstone floor and whitewashed walls. Carrie skilfully skimmed cream from shallow earthenware pancheons. Spring calvers and new grass provided golden cream for rich yellow butter, salty and patterned with clover leaves. Hannah leaned from her window, cloth in hand. Outside on the line, curtains danced as they dried. Spring stirred in the garden, thrusting in tufts and spikes of many-shaded green. Carrie opened the gate and walked past the forsythia, a cloth-covered basket on her arm. A white apron covered most of the Butter Lady's blue dress, the tapes meeting in a final bow at the front. Last year's best hat, beige straw with a pink rose, was rammed rather unsuitably on her head. She had never really liked it, always feeling that the assistant in Millinery had over-persuaded her, gushing about how well it suited "Modom". Seated at the mirror, making what her daughter called her "hat-face" she had tried on dozens from the pink table, then from the brown and the beige. A glance at her watch and the impending departure of her bus had scurried her into a choice she had since regretted. . .

"Take your time, lovey!" Mrs. Lundy advised, recalling that the merits of a carrot or a "window-breaker" top always needed unhurried consideration and serious thought. The expenditure of a few pence knife-bladed from a piggy-bank's hard-saved store must never be rushed.

In the dusty, sun-speckled lane, Susie hurled the thong-twirled top into exhilarating life. On its metal tip it whirled down the street between the cottages, juddering over the rough places; it teetered in the gravelly gutter, wobbled precariously and was only just saved from collapse on the grass bank. Only once did Susie halt its splendid progress, holding it fondly in her hand to allow the passage of a farm cart, with Sammy smiling and waving from the shaft.

Winter-rough store cattle thronged the pens. The Auctioneer, husky from several hours' competition with loud-bawling beast, sold lot after lot. At the Black Swan beer-happy drovers agreed terms with the buyers and set off, guiding their charges to new fields and farms. Unkempt dogs pranced about their Masters' heels, snapping, snarling, then slinking ahead at command to guard gaps and turnings.

DOWN WITH MOSLEY, someone had emphatically chalked on a partly demolished wall. Daniel in his rag-tattery coat, string-belted, his boot studs clattering on the cobbles, passed by unheeding, with his bearded face set towards the country. He knew and wished to know nothing of politics. This was his simple life . . . a fine bunch of steers ahead, a wise dog to translate his bidding and only the scribble of a flock of starlings upon a flame-streaked evening sky.

The Camp

An asthmatic brown lorry, lumpy-laden, rattled through the village. Beside the driver sat Connie, Captain of the 1st Cathedral Company of Girl Guides. Connie's elbow leaned on the open window, thus slightly easing the cramped space and also allowing the pleasant rush of cooling air so welcomed by her damp red face and by her bulging body, tightly packaged as it was in navy blue serge.

Past a row of cottages and a farm-house; after a few shunts the lorry was manoeuvred through a gateway scarcely wider than itself. William had left the gate expectantly open and the liberated vehicle bounced over dry grass like a Shire released to pasture, lurched momentarily into winter's hard-moulded ruts and then, panting, across to the camp-site field. There, with gently steaming radiator, it rested.

A following straggle of haversacked and excited girls wheeled their cycles into the field, led by four patrol leaders with lanyards and tape-striped pockets who bore the understandable bossiness of third year summer camp veterans. Vera, the young Lieutenant, newly promoted from the Cadets, came last of all.

By four o'clock Bill was waving from his cab and the empty lorry, quenched and refreshed, turned back towards town. The load had become six ridge tents against a dry-stone wall, a fat bell tent and several well-labelled tea chests and miscellaneous heaps still pending. The necessary trench, dug earlier by William and Guttridge, was decently screened by hessian and coyly occupied the farthest corner of the site, huddled with a couple of attendant wash tents. Guides and Guiders now wore camp overalls of informal blue cotton; the first tea had been brewed and hunks of margarine and plum-jammed bread filled a white enamel tray. New campers, finicky, searched the jam for imprisoned flying insects, the milk for smuts from the fire, and the grass for remaining signs of the sheep that William had taken to fresh grazing a while ago. Daphne grimaced over her first mouthful of outdoor tea. Captain had, in fact, doubted the pampered child's ability to enjoy camp life but now cheerfully reminded her that smoky tea was just a tiny difficulty under which a good Guide must endeavour to smile and sing.

Last year Beryl had been amongst those who rather wistfully played improvised rounders in the afternoons, her struggling few breast-strokes across the indoor baths insufficient to allow her safely to join the others at the bathing place. So all through last winter she had practised and improved, stoically suffered the instruction given by a fierce teacher whose strident voice echoed harshly around her chlorined domain. With protesting lungs Beryl surface-dived to retrieve a rubber brick; she learned to life save and (sometimes much worse) to be "saved" herself. Her reward was a Bronze Medal and now the freedom of the disused quarry. A younger group set out the bean bags for rounders' bases, chased the ball into nettles and thorns and enviously watched the swimmers.

The water was cold and had a dreadful depth, as black as the cliff of slate that rose behind it. Bare feet padded among the moss and unfurling bracken, then gratefully onto the sun-warmed plank that was fixed as a diving board. The long descent through the water was at first terrifying, then the ascent seemed never-ending. The eventual bubbling back into the bright world was relief beyond imagination. Beryl was pleased to think of her nervous mother safely at home, with no idea of her present activity. Vera swam with the girls while Captain stood by with a ready-coiled life-line, her wrist-watch ticking away the ten minutes whose passing was marked by a peremptory blast from her whistle.

Robin Patrol fetched milk from the farm, kicking happily through long grass until their sandals were yellow-dusted with buttercup pollen. Steady thrumming came from the low cowshed where William and Mrs. William were busy at afternoon milking, seated on three-legged stools apparently quite calm when the great cows jiffled their feet and swished their tails, irritated by biting flies. A star-burst of rangy cats lapped from an upturned churn lid then scattered in high-tailed alarm at this invasion of strangers. These were not the somnolent, purring pets of home but yard cats, unfriendly, half-wild, that worked for their living and slaked their thirst for their wages. Milk ran twisting from the cooler as Mrs. William filled the two cans, enquired whether they had everything they needed and kindly promised them some peas from the garden for to-morrow's lunch. Chaffinch Patrol worked at their camp gadgets, shoe racks, hanging racks and a clothes line. Sally had chosen two stout, straightish sticks from a pile near the wall. Taking the knife from her belt she opened it, shuddering as the springy resistance of the big blade threatened to bend back her thumbnail. Sitting cross-legged on the ground she whittled the ends into points so the supports could be hammered into the ground with the tent peg mallet. Then she attached the line, shortening it afterwards with a neat sheepshank secured with small toggles of wood. Mary, second of the Larks, was tussling with porridge pan sludge. Vera carefully raised the dixie lid . . . bubbles just pocked the surface of the water, ready for the suet puddings that Captain was tying down in their basins.

Wednesday dawned scowling through a purple sky, breathing with a wet westerly wind. "Her'll be a weather-breeder . . ." William pessimistically announced when he came to offer the use of his barn. So, in the early showering of a dismal day, Guides clad in cycle-capes and sou'-westers flapped and floundered downhill like an exotic flock of yellow wading birds exulting in the rain.

The stone barn was high and old, its rafters festooned with ancient forgotten ropes and rusted chains, with stowed and rotting sacks and the swagged webs of spider'd years. Guttridge stitched fleeces into a canvas wool-sheet that was conveniently suspended between chaff-cutter and grinding mill. He rammed his fist to consolidate the greasy, reeking cargo . . . his other hand painfully held taut the previous stitch stabbed by a hooked needle that drew thin waxed cord. His task almost finished, he made an angry, retaining backstitch, tetchily warned the girls not to meddle — and stumped off through the rain to the harness room.

"No telling", he sourly complained to young Bob as they shared their mid-morning snap, "what they lasses'll be up to. There'll be chaff and oats littered everywhere, I'll be bound." Polly ignored certain mysterious scuffles, feeling more confident when Captain pointed out the raftered rows of sheltering, preening sparrows and consequently less imaginative of skittering mice or even of coarse-haired, whip-tailed rats.

Shoes were Sunday-polished, belts and badges gleamed on best uniforms; coloured patrol ribbons floated gaily from shoulders and eyes were shaded by wide-brimmed navy felt hats. Towards a glad peal of summoning bells a proud column marched along the sycamore lane to Church. Josie tried so hard not to feel conceited but this, for her, was the best part of the whole week. Soldier-smart, she carried the Colour, escorted by Monica and Elaine. Never was sky so blue, grass so summer-green, never a little girl's life so good.

Parson took the Colour and laid it reverently upon the altar, between two tall brass vases filled with lupins. This was the fifteenth successive year of Guide camps, he mused, although his ageing mind was becoming a little fuddled, events time-fogged in his memory. *"Onward, Christian Soldiers"* sang choir and congregation. Captain read the Lesson and Parson preached a rambling sermon, incomprehensively woven around shining brass buttons and the Good Book. Josie searched for its meaning; patriotism, religion and emotion intermingled in her mind. She gazed at the sapphire robe of a stained glass Saint . . . and decided to be a Nun when she left school.

Helen's careful fingers methodically arranged the dry fragments of punk, collected in the spinney. There were delicate curls of silver birch bark, almost too glossy, too silken, to burn. Next were corky slivers of crumbling wood riddled with holes, some dry grass and a double handful of last autumn's crackly brown leaves. Over this she built a wigwam of kindling and then thicker pieces in decreasing, criss-crossed squares. Finally she roofed it with a layer of twigs and small branches. Sitting back on her heels she surveyed and checked, then went to fetch Captain to observe the lighting ceremony. Striking a one-chance match she let it splutter into life before thrusting it into the heart of her tinder-dry edifice. A wisp of smoke filtered to the top. Helen watched with horror as, despite her crossed fingers, it dwindled . . .

"Blow on it, quickly!" Captain encouraged her. The child's cheeks ached with effort, until suddenly a venturesome young flame burst through, crackling the twigs as it fed upon them and grew strong. "Well done," smiled the older woman, and Helen watched rapturously as her creation blazed before her and another test was vanquished.

Day-heat had been enveloping. Coolness came with sunset; the flag was hauled down and "Taps" was sung in the sweet shades of evening.

Camp-fire leapt with great rioting flames. Monica's back, blanket-wrapped, felt shivery . . . partly from the breeze and partly from the niggling feeling that some unknown thing might be there behind the stone wall,

C.C.

something formless and nameless that had crept from the wood across the paddock. She glanced around, hotched nearer to the fire-lit circle and pulled the blanket comfortingly higher. Captain inserted ashwood into the blaze, dislodging the grey ghost-shapes of logs already spent. Lieutenant Vera conducted the girls in a rousing, tumbling round — "*Camp fire's burning! Camp fire's burning!*" began the Robins, softly. The verse swelled then diminished, with the Sparrows finishing appropriately with "*And pass round the cocoa!*" Enamel mugs were hot in clasping hands . . . Maisie's had a chipped rim that gave a metallic taste against her lips. Daphne, in only four days, had discovered that a whiff of wood-smoke could magically, unexpectedly turn cocoa into nectar.

Drowsiness eventually overcame the hardness of the ground. Joan sacrificed her pillow to pad the worst place where her hip-bone was growing numb. She cushioned her deprived head with her hand instead, and dozed. Pam wrapped cold feet in a jumper until the recesses of her sleeping-bag felt warm at last.

Flashlight beams ceased their climbing explorations of tent walls.

In dew-spangled stillness, as night changed to moonlit morning, a fox-shadow sped low through a gap in the fence, lifting its nose to scent the promise of small, scurrying creatures. It passed close by the group of tents, leaving long slurred paw prints in the silvery grass. The 1st Cathedral Company, sleeping, saw nothing. . .

Percy

Percy sat on the doorstep of his hut, carefully mending a broken bootlace, thus extending its already overlived life. His task satisfactorily finished he raised his arms and leaned his head comfortably against locked fingers. He yawned. For a while he wallowed drowsily in the benevolence of September sunshine.

The remains of an old Austin hid on perished tyres amongst nettles that were tall and rank, tasselled with dark flowers. Here Percy had left it, at the terminus of its final journey some seven years ago. No amount of cranking had roused the engine since, although the bonnet was still pathetically raised as a memorial to Percy's occasional efforts. Fence stakes, rusty milk-churns, a mouse-ridden roll of rotting binder-canvas and some bottomless buckets rested on the collapsed seats, burst through broken windows and partially supported a swag of mouldering grey roof-lining.

A great heap of wood was dumped, mossed and green, wrapped with long, dead tentacles of many grassy summers. Nearby was a derelict saw-table once carted, when still usable, from a sale. Somehow, wood and saw had never been brought together, bouts of lassitude having constantly defeated Percy's enthusiasm for producing bags of logs for sale.

White butterflies tossed, fluttering, above a row of lacy cabbages that were ravaged by green, feasting caterpillars. Persicaria and fat-hen, couch grass and dead nettles romped in riotous carnival, smothering carrots and beetroot, even threatening the few sickly potatoes that bravely struggled to grow in cloddy, half-worked soil.

Hens bathed in their dust-bowls, then preened and fluffed their brown feathers. Percy, watching them, stood up and fetched a basket from the shed. The chicken hut was stuffy and dark, pervaded by ammonia-stench

Colin Carr

from accumulated droppings beneath the perches. A hunched hen, eyes closed, stood dejectedly in a corner. Percy cursed as he collected only two eggs, finding a third one broken, stained with filth and dried yolk . . . the culprit ran gawkily behind a forest of thistles; companions chased her, expecting a taste of the prize that dangled, dripping, from her beak. Later Percy must fill a decoy shell with mustard.

Back in his shed he burrowed like a mole among layers of hoarded rubbish that was maturing into usefulness. Somewhere he had seen a salvaged copy of a poultry magazine . . . maybe it could diagnose the trouble with his ailing hen. Instead he found a tin full of old spectacles with thin gold rims that had once encircled eyes now long unseeing. There in a smaller box was another treasure, a knob of yellow chalk. Percy wrote a large "A" on the wall, then rows of random, diminishing letters. One by one, placing each aside after use with methodical care, he hooked the spectacles over his ears and played, as seriously as a child, at opticians.

Next he cleaned with a piece of rag the cracked mirror that hung near the hut door . . . and studied himself. He removed his cap and smoothed the sparse grey hair across his balding head. His face was clean-shaven, shiny and pink, and a thin neck stuck out from a striped flannelette shirt whose neckband was fastened by a gleaming brass stud. Opening his mouth he examined the black cavity in a tooth. To-day it did not ache. To-morrow he might have to soothe it with a cotton-wool pellet soaked in whisky. Eventually it would break off, or perhaps loosen and drop out as others had previously done. Rather would he bear these possibilities than face a visit to the dental surgery in town, there to submit to the terrifying unknown.

Just then Percy noticed something odd about his ramshackle tractor, protected as it was by an old carpet and a torn coat secured by twine. Its treadless tyres were shielded from sun by old sacks . . . but the empty fruit tin that should have covered the exhaust had gone. Percy scrabbled on the ground, then scratched his head and plodded, puzzled, around the precious vehicle. At last he selected a stubby paint-brush and sought a partly dried puddle of paint in the bottom of a tin.

Along the middle rail of his broken gate and overflowing across the edge of the iron bedstead that filled the gapped hedge, he wrote his warning to those without authority to enter. "PRIVATE", he wrote. "NO TRESPASSERS" and then, for emphasis, "KEEP OUT". He stood back to admire his work. The scrawled words pleased him, effectively soothing away the annoyance that had caused their creation.

Gifts

Mist swirled across the yard, distorting sight and sound. Majestic corn stacks, their fat sides bristling with thousand-butted sheaves, loomed like ships from sea fog. Perhaps foghorns were booming dolefully above the wash and surge of sighing tide; maybe those were wreckers' lights instead of bleary-eyed hurricane lamps that swung, hand-high, from barn to cowshed and back to stable and fold as Walter and Claud completed their evening work.

Never until the last cow had been milked and strawed down, the latest bawling calf hushed by its slurped half bucket of dam-warm milk . . . never until Claud had turned his cycle for the cottage in the village and Walter's boot-studs had rasped, metal to metal on the scraper . . . never until then did Milly draw the curtains. Then was the kitchen enclosed, safe, rosy-warm in mature fireglow, gently lit by benison of the beautiful lamp. Walter's slippers were warming by the steel fender; to-morrow's kindling was neatly piled in the hearth. Later, when pots were washed and the cutlery back in the dresser drawer, when Walter, drugged by warmth after the cold day's slog, dozed in his chair, then Milly returned to her task . . .

Sally's favourite doll had a soft body, with arms bunched at the wrists to form pudgy, fingerless hands; she had dangly legs and her once-smiling face was smooth-smudged by a lifetime of cuddles. Her measurements, secretly taken last summer, were recorded behind the calendar and now Milly was translating them into a green silk dress with lacy collar and also into a blue topcoat with shiny buttons. In her scrap bag there was enough floral winceyette for a nightie . . . she would tuck the bodice and make a shell-edged hem. She planned a pink cardigan, maybe a jumper and skirt. A twisted

skein of baby wool tucked away in her workbox would
become a ribbed vest and matching pilch. Milly's nimble
hands sped with her thoughts . . . there was much to be
done in the next few weeks, before the family's Christmas visit.

★   ★   ★

Wood-curls fell fragrantly about Reuben's feet and a
breathy whistle accompanied the swish of the plane that
produced them. The shelf was tried, then planed, then
tried and planed again until eventually it suited even
Reuben's stern requirements. The Vicar's wife would be

pleased when it was ready and she could place in it the set of wild flower books that she had bought for the Vicar's birthday in December. Together she and Reuben had discussed the design, even to the bit of carving with which the old craftsman would embellish the ends, thus making it truly recognisable as his special, caring work. She looked forward with pleasure to seeing the blue-and-gold bound books displayed against the dark shelves. Just there, in the study, after the serious business of preparing his sermon was over, the Vicar would choose one of the volumes and take it across to his leather-clad chair by the fire. She could imagine the reverent way in which he would so carefully turn the pages, the delighted smile with which he would greet each colour plate and the quiet enjoyment with which his scholarly mind would feast upon page after page of solid botanical information.

The junk shop smelt fusty, dusty, as though drily rotting away for want of light and air. A vast table was burdened with past tea services, enamel candlesticks, brassware and precarious piles of odd, chipped plates. All about the floor, where no broom encroached and where any disturbance sent beetles scuttling for cover, were job lots with sale numbers still sticking to them . . . saucepans blackened from cottage fires, framed texts and big earthenware crocks.

Little Hickory himself merged into his background, appearing unexpectedly from some webbed corner when a customer arrived. His plucked-chicken neck stuck from a worn shirt whose sleeves were rolled above sinewy, bluish arms. He had spiky brown hair and, surprisingly, a waxed moustache. His hands were shiny-grimed, black from rummaging among his stock, from stacking books and old newspapers and, some said, from constantly counting and gloating over the coins that were kangaroo-pocketed in his hessian apron . . . Hickory mistrusted banks, distributing his reputed wealth among a collection of tea tins, fibre suitcases and padlocked tin trunks.

Once, it was whispered, some resident mice had nested royally in chewed white fivers that Hickory had hidden under a loose floor board in his attic.

Mother had taken her list to the grocer's down the street, leaving Amy and Pauline (in their well-buttoned-up brown tweed coats, thick three-quarter socks and good winter shoes) to do their secret shopping. "Plenty of time, me dears, plenty of time!" Hickory told them as they searched. Amy giggled, involuntarily but politely behind a hasty hand . . . this was one of the junkman's famous sayings. Time, indeed, was all around as a crowd of clocks measured away the minutes. There was the plodding time of a grandfather with the sun and moon on its painted face, the runaway chatter of an oak mantel clock and the sweet ticking of a silver pocket watch that whispered confidingly into a closely-held ear.

Amy, at first, chose a plaster figure of a lady in pink crinoline and lavender poke-bonnet. Little Pauline had removed her hat. Being rather tight it had made a red mark on her forehead and, as she told her sister, "It stops me finking". Unhampered and thus again able to think, she soon found a graceful white vase encrusted with blue forget-me-nots. Hickory, pocketing her shilling, carefully wrapped the purchase in a crumply piece of elderly tissue paper.

Amy quickly replaced her ornament when a string of crystal beads sparkled at her from a cardboard lid. "Only want a soapy wash, me dear, and they'll look like diamonds!" The diamonds, (a whole one-and-three-pence worth), were rolled into a page torn from *Picture Post*. The girls skipped out into the street, their gifts hidden in Amy's brown paper carrier . . . which Mother pretended not to notice, even though it was large enough to flap against Amy's legs.

★   ★   ★

Bobby wrapped the eiderdown cosily around his shoulders and back, the blankets closely over his humped knees . . . only his hands remained slightly cold. He had tried wearing his woolly gloves but found it impossible to write. The flashlight propped beside him gave a circle of yellow light, poorly illuminating the ruled page upon which he was painstakingly scribing his poem, each letter slowly formed as the rough draft, with all its alterations and afterthoughts, its laboured then less-laboured rhymes, gradually became "The Bluebell Wood". With crayons, a border would be coaxed into bloom, unseasonably, to decorate the page. Bobby yawned; his eyelids heavy over sleepy eyes . . . to-morrow he could finish his present, perhaps while Mother was feeding the hens. He pushed pad and crayons under the pillow and snuggled into the eiderdown.

The flashlight, forgotten, struggled bravely on through the night. Then, at dawning, it died.

The Bone Setter

L uke enjoyed his winter digging. His patten'd boot drove the sharp spade cleanly into the ground, turning a brown chunk into line with its predecessors. To-day's work should complete the preparation of his garden to receive the benison of frost. An icy wind bore down from the north-east, a lazy wind that threatened to go through instead of around him. It pierced the thick corduroy of trousers that were fastened rat-catcher style with band at the ankles . . . it tested the indestructible serge of jumble-sale waistcoat and jacket. But hard work gave warmth that surged through his body, made glowing pink the pleasant face encircled by its knitted balaclava. He whistled, pausing at each row end to tidy his nose with the back of his hand . . . and briefly to rest and plan. Shallots here, tates there; carrots and beetroot; Esther's favourite beans and plenty of parsnips and onions. Ideas were roughly scrawled to fill the notepad of his mind, already rich with the experience of many seasons that now sped unbelievably fast; slumb'rous winter would, he knew, so soon awaken into busy, bustling spring. A dunnock, mole-brown, searched the hedge bottom; she was scarcely noticeable among the leaf-mould, but enchanted the man with her shy, companionable presence.

Pearl from Mill Cottage leaned her bike against the privet hedge that was hugely and anciently solid, clipped by Luke into two splendid cockerels and a masterpiece of spiralling cones.

"Terrible job I've had getting here!" she complained. "My foot's that bad I scarcely knew how to press the pedal . . ."

Esther, Luke's sister, was ironing; she took a fresh flat-iron from the grid before the red fire in the range, replacing it with the cooling one. Her iron-holder was of navy blue felt with a red corded edging and a loop to hang it by . . . when not in use it occupied a hook together with her bright green pin-cushion and sturdy steel scissors. She spat on the iron and tiny globules frantically danced on its searing surface . . . satisfied, she wiped it on a hessian cloth and smeared it across a block of beeswax. Fragrance of hot cotton rose as another sheet was smoothed on her board; the airer was filling with folded clothes, row upon fire-warmed row. A gentle bubbling came from the black pot, where a bacon hock was coddling with turnips and potatoes . . .

Pearl's anxious face peered through the steam-misted window. Esther saw her above the aspidistra and between the brown plush curtains and immediately reached to unlatch the door.

The troublesome foot rested on a stool in the parlour. The room was sidling-full of ponderous furniture, crammed with photographs and ornaments on crocheted white mats. Each piece of burnished brass had a tiny blazing fire at its heart and the window was primly lace-curtained against nosey folk with prying eyes. Esther puddled liniment into her palm, rubbed her fingers diagnostically down each side of Pearl's ankle; she gently waggled and rotated it, then, with firmer pressure, produced an audible and reassuring click.

"There," she confidently pronounced, "that'll be better in no time. Come back in a week and I'll lock it for you."

Pearl's first tentative steps were slightly less difficult. She was one of the faithful; her trust enhanced the mystical power of Esther's hands and would certainly ensure her recovery. A shilling joined the coins already stowed in the toffee tin on the sideboard . . . the black Scottie dog growled softly from under the table (as was his way with all departing clients). His mistress scolded him, simultaneously appeasing him with a biscuit from her apron pocket.

Esther's gift had been inherited from her Grandmother and Great-Grandmother . . . her own Mother, strangely, had never been "blessed". Sceptics could not be guaranteed a cure; those who left their limps behind, whose ligaments were firmly replaced and twists and sprains straightened, tended to be the believers.

A statuesque stranger from town had once arrived at Esther's cottage, driven in a fine purring car that drew all the village children out in the lane to gape. She regally occupied the back as though her small pale husband, swamped by a bowler hat, were merely the chauffeur. Winding down her window she had informed Luke in a haughty contralto that she had been over-persuaded by a gullible friend, although she herself regarded bone-setters as charlatans practising a lot of mumbo-jumbo. "However, my man," she concluded, "escort me to this sister of yours as I wish her to look at my shoulder." Luke's usually mild manner shook savagely within him. Stuttering with temper and jerking a commanding thumb towards the town he told her to clear off back home and take her shoulder with her. The woman, so Luke related for years afterwards, had wound up her window, wrapped her fur collar protectively around her. Then, prodding her amazed husband in the back with her kid-gloved finger, she had ordered him to drive away fast from this uncouth yokel . . .

Squire had provided the pony trap for Esther when lumbago had suddenly attacked, threatening to fell him

where he stood. She went equipped with an unopened
bottle of liniment, a large cabbage leaf and some clean red
flannel. Whether from manipulation, from the cabbage
leaf poultice or the warm wrap, or whether as the result
of several days' enforced rest, Squire never knew. But
one afternoon he arose painlessly from his bed and
walked freely and joyously across the room. Thoughtless
in his delight he sent a bottle of old sherry with his
thanks, which were duly acknowledged on Esther's best
mauve notepaper. But the sherry was stored, untouched,
in a dim corner of the attic, well wrapped in brown paper
and draped with a piece of material to disguise its evil
shape. A pious woman, Esther had been strictly brought
up by Wesleyan parents . . . she and Luke atended
Chapel twice every Sunday, carrying large Prayer Books
and sitting stiffly on cruelly uncomfortable pews, patiently absorbing the longest of tedious sermons for the good
of their souls. Esther loved and regularly read her Bible,
kept the Sabbath and hoped, humbly, for an eventual
golden life in Heaven. But the sherry worried her. She
dared not dispose of it for fear of offending the Squire, but
it was the subject of many uneasy and apologetic prayers.

No matter what ailment required treating, Esther could prescribe a herbal remedy. Her dark oak corner cupboard was wealthy with mysterious bottles, corked or glass-stoppered; dumpy jars held buttercup ointment, goose-grease or sweet-smelling salves for hands and weather-battered faces. She grew palliative plants in a garden patch and collected more from the fields and woods . . . she dried and mixed and infused. Her teas and potions were famous, both for their unpalatability and their efficacy. For children she kindly added honey or blackcurrant, maybe a drop or two of peppermint essence. Despite this she had, among timid youngsters, the reputation for being a witch. Fortunately she was chubby-dimpled . . . even without her teeth her buttony nose came nowhere near her chin; her cat was an amiable ginger tabby and her sweeping brush as normal as any housewife's. Nevertheless, children were prone to peep fearfully into corners, expecting to see propped-up besoms ready for flight, and one small boy had run home in howling terror because an extra large toad had crawled from wet grass beside Luke's garden path.

Esther was weary, as always after doing her ironing. Candlelight flickered her reflection as she brushed with a silver brush the white hair that had drifted, loose and long, from its daytime pins. Her beige dressing-gown was thick, but still she shivered as she knelt beside the bed. *Thou, God, seest me!* warned the sombre text, decorated and framed upon the wall . . . and He saw, no doubt, the sherry (for the possession of which she yet again sincerely asked forgiveness). Then she climbed into her narrow iron bed.

Downstairs, Luke removed his boots and, when he had drunk his cocoa, brewed thick as mud, he locked and noisily bolted the door.

The Travelling Fair

Walter carefully pulled shallots from dry earth, admiring each brown-clad cluster and enjoying their papery rustle and the pungent smell that rose to his nostrils. As his wife tenderly removed crusty loaves and risen sponges from the oven, viewing perfection as it nestled between her cloth-wrapped hands, so Walter knew quiet pride in the results of his work. On his birthday in February he had planted the single bulbs that now so bounteously had multiplied into harvest. "Plant on February Day to lift on Fair Day", he told Mary's lads, and they looked at each other and grinned . . . for this was but one of Grandad's sayings, small treasures of golden wisdom somewhat dulled by wrappings of familiarity.

Between the hedges, past the Vicarage and under the yellowing ash trees, moved a procession burdened by the cumbersome panoply of the Fair. Great gaudy lorries spluttered fumes as they dragged, choking, at shrouded trailers; sawn-off Land Rovers drew loads humped and mysterious under black tarpaulins; a paunchy man in gangster trilby and chalk-striped suit manoeuvred the first of four gleaming living vans, setting the fancy curtain nets shuddering as he jolted through the gateway into Poor Land's Paddock.

From the far end of the village the dogs began to bark; children gaped in wonderment, afraid of the huge noise. Walter and his contemporaries beamed as though mesmerised by warm, enveloping nostalgia. Watched from windows and doors, from gardens and barns and straw stacks, slowly with all the majestic dignity of yesterday, progressed the mighty steam engine. Ponderously, vibrating the ground with the thunder of iron wheels, it took its appointed place as Monarch of the Fair.

Sally dipped her face into a cloud of candy floss, gossamer sugar that pink-blobbed her nose and chin, ethereal wisps that became sweetly gritty between her small white teeth. She was bumped by Tommy and Dick from the top class who were hurtling from coconut shy to rifle range, bouncing among the crowds. The two boys stamped their feet and shouted, waved their arms in a fever of tumult and excitement, delirious from the mingled smells of canvas and rope, creosote and crushed sow-thistles, and of the diesel waste that belched from throbbing generators. Then suddenly came a gust of frying onions and that would eventually lead them to the hot dog stall where glistening sausages cooked crisp and brown, where a priestess-woman worked deft-handed with rolls and knife, anointing them with dobs of yellow mustard or glutinous ketchup from crimson-dribbled jars.

Walter cared nothing for the cacophony of the Fair, nor for the stalls and rides. But his face wore an easy smile, his faded blue eyes were moist behind round, gold-rimmed spectacles and he drew long and happily at his pipe. All whirled and gyrated around him unnoticed, colourless and silent save for this creature of steam and belts and harnessed hissing power. In a group they stood, Walter and George and Harry too, wrapt with memories that needed no words.

"Monarch" was dressed in gleaming maroon; barley sugar twists of brass held aloft his canopy; his massive wheels lurched in their ruts as though he lived and, living, wished to be free. Perhaps he felt foolish as he powered the exquisite Gavidi organ that looked so fragile on a trailer beside him. As though made of porcelain it was, blue as summer sky and adorned with fat cherubs that played gilded trumpets or slender silver flutes. There were flowers looped and garlanded, extravagant flourishes and delicate scrollwork. Punched cardboard concertina'd into folds behind as each familiar tune reached its last rousing bars.

Stevie threw darts at impaled cigarette packets on a stall. He fancied that they ricocheted, jumping back far more than ever they did from the old board in the shed at home where, with practice, he had become quite skilled. A morose youth, gold rings dangling from ears lost among greasy hair, and sleeves rolled to expose tattooed arms, passed him three more darts in exchange for his pocket-warmed coin . . . then callously poured tea from a flask when dreams thudded with the final luckless spear to the boarded floor. A blatantly orange teddy leered at him, saucer-eyed; boxed watches and amber-coloured vases, all the trashy opulence from Hong Kong, were blurred as Stevie tried to stroll away. Nonchalance was crushed under heavy disappointment and a brave whistle turned to soundless breath from trembling lips.

Giggling girls jostled each other through the booth door. Madame Zarella thrust a sandwich back into her bag, wiped her hands on her crumpled Eastern skirt and pushed the bangles further up her brown-stained arms. She spread and stabbed red-clawed fingers in a mystic dance above the crystal ball that furnished the cloth-covered table before her. Vaguely anatomical charts of heads and palms flapped with the canvas; somehow disturbed, the first of the girls listened to a muttered rigmarole, she and Madame imprisoned under a light of eerie-green in an aroma of stale cigarette smoke.

Liz stood entranced as the merry-go-round revolved faster and faster, to the accompaniment of wild squeals from its passengers and a squeaky waltz from the nearby organ. Up and down, round and round, went the beautiful dappled horse with its flaring red nostrils and shining black hooves, ever followed by a cockerel resplendent in purple and scarlet and blue, then an emerald dragon with copper-edged scales and dreadful flaming eyes. She would never dare to ride, up there where you whirled and whirled and couldn't stop, and you clung to the handles or desperately clasped a wooden neck. Perhaps in a crescendo of music you flew far from the stand, away from the fading painted wood, away to a magical land of nowhere on a prancing, snorting, silver horse.

Dick and Harry regularly lurked the lanes and roamed the fields, earning ammunition with the rabbits they shot, felling the ragged rooks from tall elms, or picking off the stockies that fed on the peas. Thus trained they now confidently aimed at a fantasy parade of Disney ducks and roguish rabbits, finding their demise as difficult as had been the dislodging of brown, bearded coconuts at the shy.

As evening came the whole fair was spangled by sparkling lights, jewels that scintillated as they swung in the breeze and made a hazy halo against the black trees and surrounding fields. To-morrow would come the dismantling and the start of the journey towards winter quarters; away would rumble the whole procession over the hill to the turnpike road.

In Walter's garden the shallots would lie, neatly rowed, to dry in the Autumn sun . . .